By A. Hyatt Verrill

STRANGE STORIES FROM NATURE SERIES

Strange Animals and Their Stories

Strange Birds and Their Stories

Strange Creatures of the Sea

Strange Fish and Their Stories

Strange Insects and Their Stories

Strange Prehistoric Animals

Strange Reptiles and Their Stories

Strange Sea Shells and Their Stories

Strange Story of Our Earth

Foods America Gave the World

Minerals, Metals and Gems

My Jungle Trails

Perfumes and Spices

Strange Customs, Manners and Beliefs

The Incas' Treasure House

L. C. Page & Company · Publishers · 53 Beacon Street, Boston

Strange Stories from Nature Series

STRANGE CREATURES OF THE SEA

Key to color illustration on following page:

1. Velella jellyfish

2. Moon jellyfish

3. Sea lily, or crinoid

4. Branching sponge

5. Glove, or finger sponge

6-7. Tube sponges

8. Swimming crab

9. Sea whip, or gorgonian

10-11-12. Sea anemones

13. Zoanthus

14. Sea puddings, or ascidians

15. Sea peaches, or sea squirts (ascidians)

16. Gaudy starfish (Florida)

STRANGE CREATURES

of the SEA

A. HYATT VERRILL

illustrated by the author

L. C. PAGE & COMPANY

BOSTON *Publishers*

Table of Contents

made. Internal anatomy. A hydraulic power plant. Basket starfish. Serpent stars.

List of Illustrations

Introduction

Introduction

FEW persons realize the vast number of strange creatures that inhabit the sea. Fish, crabs, lobsters, and shrimp; starfish, sea urchins, sand worms, and jellyfish; whales, porpoises, sea turtles, squids, and octopuses; corals, sponges, sea fans, and sea anemones are all perhaps familiar forms of marine life to those who dwell near or visit the seashore. But these, numerous as they are, form but a small fraction of the denizens of the oceans. People more or less familiar with the better-known marine animals usually possess only a cursory knowledge of the lives and habits of the sea creatures.

They know that clams, oysters, scallops and a few other shellfish are prized as food, that clams live in the sand or mud, that oysters attach themselves to rocks or other objects, and they may know that scallops can swim. They realize that there are many kinds of crabs; that some are delectable food, while others are deemed worthless. They may know that "shedder"—soft-shelled—crabs are those that have just cast off their hard shells, and for a time are soft and tender. They know that lobsters are delicious eating and are caught in pots, or traps. They know that sponges, having been dried and cleaned, are used for washing everything from our bodies to our automobiles. They may even know that starfish are enemies of oysters and destroy the bivalves.

Even if they have never seen a living coral, sea fan, or sea rod, they may have seen them in curio shops and museums, and they may have seen and admired the flowerlike sea anemones, or may have used marine worms or sand hoppers for baiting fishhooks. However, only those who have taken a keen interest in the creatures of the sea realize how amazing are the lives and habits of even the most familiar sea animals. Only such people are familiar with the vast number of forms of marine creatures that remain unknown to the average person, and the highly important part these creatures play in our lives, fisheries, and foods.

Wildlife on land—where it has not been destroyed by man—is exceedingly abundant, varying from gigantic elephants to microscopic insects. Many of its forms are of incalculable value to man and his industries; fully as many are man's enemies, to be destroyed whenever possible. Yet compared to life in the sea, wildlife on land is scarce, even in the areas most favorable for its development. Moreover, the innumerable forms of creatures that inhabit the land are far easier to study than those in the sea. Although great numbers of marine animals inhabit shallow water, where they are accessible to anyone, by far the larger number dwell in deep water and can only be taken for study by means of dredges, trawls, and other devices. But for every known form of deep-sea marine life, there are undoubtedly thousands that no scientist has ever seen.

Dragging a dredge or a trawl over the bottom of the ocean beneath hundreds of fathoms of water may be compared to cruising in a space ship twelve miles or more above the earth and dragging a huge net across the country. One might capture a few birds, some of the larger and less active quadrupeds, some insects and other forms of life; but the chances of catching wary, fleet-footed creatures, human beings or animals who inhabit dense forests, caverns, or rugged mountains, would be almost nil. So the dredges and trawls that our scientists drag over the ocean floor, miles below the surface, capture only a few of the countless forms of life inhabiting the vast depths. Even so, the creatures they have secured are often as strange and interesting as a human being, a dog, or a cat would be to a Martian.

It is fortunate for those interested in the lives and habits of sea creatures that we do not have to seek all of them in the abysmal depths of the oceans. Within easy reach of almost anyone—at almost any spot along the seashore, or in shallow water—there are enough forms of marine life to satisfy those interested in the strange sea creatures and their stories.

If you are so fortunate as to be within reach of a rocky coast where the ebbing tide leaves pools of water in the hollows of the rocks, you can find and watch a great many of the strange forms of marine life that I mention in this book. Even in the north the tide pools support an immense amount of life, and if you visit the tropics or semi-tropics—such as the Florida Keys, Bermuda, or the West Indies, where there are coral reefs—you will find countless sea creatures never found in temperate seas. You will also discover that many forms which live in northern seas are far larger and more colorful in the tropics. To find some of these sea creatures you will have to wade about in pools of water left by the tide, or on coral reefs where, hidden among the masses of dead coral in cavelike openings, the more active and wary have their homes.

Many books have been written on marine animals, but the majority of these are either technical or scientific and are of little value or interest to the average person. The purpose of this book is to tell the stories of various sea creatures, to describe their lives and habits, their homes, peculiarities, and uses in a popular, easily understood manner, as free as possible from technical terms.

Unfortunately a great many of the most interesting and useful of these creatures do not have common or English names. In such cases, where it is admissible to do so, I have given the animals English names that insofar as possible have the same meanings as the scientific Latin names. Also, a number of these creatures are known by various names, differing according to the locality. Thus a lobster of tropical and semi-tropical waters is known in Bermuda as Spanish lobster, in the Bahamas as flat lobster, and in the Lesser Antilles as sea cockroach. Sea rods, sea whips, and sea feathers are names applied to a number of the slender gorgonians. But to paraphrase Juliet: A sea creature by any other name would be as interesting.

A. Hyatt Verrill

There is many a rich stone laid up in the bowels of the earth, many a fair pearl laid up in the bosom of the sea, that never was seen, nor never shall be.

Joseph Hall, Bishop of Norwich

Strange Creatures of the Sea

1

The Most Ancient Creature

ROUGHLY a billion years ago, life first appeared upon our planet, and since at that time almost the entire sphere was covered with water, it is not surprising that the first of all living creatures should have inhabited, the sea. Although these animals, known as Protozoa, are the most ancient of all known forms of life, they still inhabit our oceans and are little changed from their ancestors of a billion years ago. Not only are the Protozoa the oldest of all animals, they are also the most numerous; a single quart of sea water may contain over a million of the tiny creatures.

They are also the simplest of all animals; each consists of a single cell, whereas other animals are composed of millions of cells. Despite their simplicity the Protozoa have a digestive system and possess means of moving about at will. Some are soft-bodied creatures, but others, known as Foraminifera, have hard lime shells, often very beautiful in form. These are made up of a number of single-celled animals united to form a single organism. Another unique feature of the Protozoa is that they do not lay eggs and have no larval forms, but reproduce by constant sub-

3

division. Although most are microscopic things, a few are plainly visible to the naked eye.

No one can possibly estimate the numbers of these creatures dwelling in the seas. They swarm in such large numbers that the skeletons or shells of the groups known as Foraminifera and Radiolaria, dropping to the bottom of the sea when these creatures die, have formed a soft, mudlike slime or ooze thousands of feet in depth and cov-

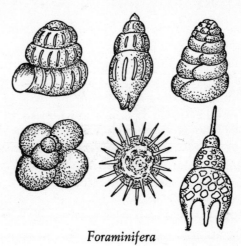

Foraminifera

ering hundreds of thousands of square miles of the ocean's floor. Despite their inconceivable numbers, one might dip up a bucket of sea water and find it as clear as crystal, yet at night the water will glow and gleam as if filled with fire, for the majority of the Protozoa are phosphorescent; although each tiny animal emits only a minute light, there are millions of the creatures in the water. Even in these days of astronomical monetary sums the human brain can scarcely conceive of the incredible numbers of protozoans existing in a small amount of sea water. Every cubic foot of sea water contains not millions, but billions of these amazing sea creatures, and a single ounce of the ooze at the bottom of the ocean contains more than three million of their skeletons.

During the ages that have passed since these creatures first appeared in the sea, great changes have taken place on our earth. Immense areas that once were at the bottom of the sea have been forced upward to become land, and the skeletal remains of the Foraminifera that once composed the ooze at the bottom of the sea became petrified and formed mountains, hills, and such chalk formations as the White Cliffs of Dover.

Although a cubic inch of chalk may contain over a million of the Protozoa shells, these are a comparatively large species. Under certain conditions of age and pressures the masses of upraised ooze became transformed to marble; if a section of the finest marble is examined under a high-powered microscope, one may detect the remains of the minute shells of the protozoans. It seems strange indeed that many of our greatest buildings, our statuary, our tombstones—even the mighty pyramids of Egypt—are all composed of the skeletons of sea creatures so small that with few exceptions they are invisible to the naked eye. And we seldom realize that whenever we use a crayon on a blackboard the white marks we make consist wholly of the crushed, fossilized shells of the Protozoa.

A single ounce of marble is composed of four or five million shells. Perhaps the modern calculating machines could give the total number of Protozoa shells in a marble table top, but yards of paper would be required to record the cyphers. Even then we would have but a very faint idea of the actual number of these animals in the sea, for the greater number have no lime shells but are soft-bodied creatures who leave no skeletons or tangible remains when they die.

To man, these most ancient and most abundant of all forms of animal life are of great economic importance and value, for their fossil remains provide us with building and ornamental stone, crayons, chalk, cleansing compounds and certain medicines.* To the denizens of the sea the living Protozoa are far more important, for they form the principal food of countless fish: lobsters, crabs, shrimp and other crustaceans; the sea anemones, corals, sponges and—perhaps strangest of all—the baleen whales.

That these largest of all living creatures should feed upon such tiny animals as the Protozoa seems not only incredible but ridiculous. However, we must not forget that it is the amount of food, rather than the size of its component parts, that counts in the end. A single grain of fine corn meal is very small compared to a man, yet a bowl of mush or a loaf of johnnycake satisfies one's appetite. You may wonder how the whales manage to catch and eat creatures that are invisible to human eyes. The answer lies in the manner by which the baleen whales feed. Unlike the sperm whales with their powerful sharp ivory teeth, the baleen whales, such as the right whale, bowhead whale, sulphur-bottom whale, gray whale, finback and others, have no teeth. Instead, their immense mouths are lined with baleen, or whalebone. Opening their enormous jaws, these whales plow through the sea, scooping up everything in the way of food that comes their way.

When their cavernous mouths are filled they close their jaws, and, using their thick muscular tongues like the plungers of a pump, they force the water out through the sievelike baleen, leaving innumerable creatures they have captured within their big mouths, ready to be gulped

* The Foraminifera are sometimes confused with the minute plants or algae known as diatoms. These have a calcareous framework and are almost as numerous as the Protozoa. Their remains form the diatomaceous earths used for polishing and for tooth powder.

down. Of course, numerically, the Protozoa exceed all
the other forms of life captured by the whales in this way,
but as far as actual bulk is concerned most of the whales'
food consists of small crustaceans, small fish, squids, jellyfish, Brachiopoda and the larval forms of shells and other
marine animals.

As thousands upon thousands of whales and other
marine animals are almost constantly eating, the total
numbers of Protozoa consumed is immeasurably beyond
human conception or imagination. But despite this cease-
less destruction, the number of Protozoa is not reduced,
for they increase as rapidly as they are destroyed or die.

Innumerable creatures have appeared upon the earth
and in the seas; they have lived, died, and become extinct.
Some have survived, but the majority of the creatures inhabiting our lands and seas are very different from their
ancestors of a few million years ago. But the minute Protozoa, the first of all forms of life to appear on the earth,
the most abundant of all creatures, have remained unchanged and undiminished in numbers. Surely if there
is truth in the theory of the "survival of the fittest," the
lowly Protozoa must be the "fittest" of all forms of life.

2

Plantlike Creatures of the Sea

IF YOU ever have picked up shells washed
upon the beach, or have turned over stones searching for
crabs and worms for bait, or have gathered seaweed, you
have doubtless seen the moss animals. There are countless
forms of these creatures of the sea; over sixteen hundred
species have been described. Often they are really beautiful; many are brilliantly colored. Some of the most
abundant and widely distributed of these animals, known
to scientists as the Bryozoa, form patches of brilliant red
incrustations on shells, rocks, corals, and even on the backs
of crabs and lobsters.

These pink, red, or orange patches are colonies of animals, for the individual creatures are very small and are
crowded together. If we examine the colonies under a microscope the animals can readily be seen. Moreover, we
will find them very lovely in form, each animal occupying an ornate tube or cell. Others are lichenlike and form
sheets of white or delicately colored lacelike growths over
rocks or other objects. Still others resemble crystals of
frost or snow. Some are hard; others are soft or slimy; still
others consist of a combination of calcareous, or lime material, and horny matter.

In addition to these matlike Bryozoa, usually mistaken for seaweed, there are the "sea mats," that look like pieces of water-soaked brown paper scattered on the beaches. When these objects are examined through a lens or a powerful reading glass we will find they are composed of many hundreds of delicate tubular cells, placed back to back in such a regular and orderly design that they appear as if stamped out by some mechanical device. Still another form of this moss animal resembles jointed seaweed. When dead and washed up on the beaches it is

Bryozoa

usually bleached white, but when alive and growing, attached to rocks and other objects under water, it is beautifully colored: rose, lilac, orange, salmon, purple, mauve or scarlet.

Some are as flexible as seaweed and wave gracefully with the currents of the water; others are stiff and jointed. Since many of these closely resemble small corals, they are commonly known as corallines. In temperate seas they are usually small and inconspicuous, but in the warmer waters of tropical and semi-tropical seas there are species that grow to a large size and are often mistaken for true corals. In fact, the so-called "pink corals" prized by visitors to the West Indies are in reality corallines, or Bryozoa.

Unfortunately there are a number of hard, calcareous sea-weeds that frequently are called "corallines," but it is a simple matter to distinguish these true plant growths from the Bryozoa if we examine them with a lens, for all the Bryozoa are composed of numerous individual cells, either cuplike or saucerlike, each of which is occupied by a living animal with slender tentacles.

Many of the branching species of these creatures are among the most delicate and beautiful of marine growths when magnified by a lens. Often they appear to be of opalescent glass blown in the most lovely forms by a master craftsman. On the delicate stems are rows of symmetrical vase-shaped cells, the open ends filled with brilliantly colored, petal-like tentacles. Others are formed of numerous cups that appear to be made of the finest porcelain; still others are composed of iridescent pearly material that shimmers with every color of the rainbow.

Among them all, none are more surprising than those of the genus *Bugula*. These have a great many branches, covered with cells that are perfect miniature birds' heads, each with its tiny beak constantly opening and closing. Watching them through a lens we can almost imagine that we hear twitters and chirps; we expect the creatures to give vent to a song.

There are other plantlike sea creatures that are even more interesting and remarkable than the Bryozoa. Like the latter, there are a myriad of forms of animals known as hydroids. Unlike the Bryozoa these creatures never form matlike incrustations but are all upright and branched; instead of being calcareous and stiff they are soft and flexible. Many so closely resemble seaweeds that they often are mistaken for them. Under a lens, however, they differ greatly from any marine plant, for the stems, branches and apparent leaves are all covered with delicate cuplike or saucerlike buds or "flowers," with a vein or tube of animal matter extending through the stalk and branches to every bud. Many of the "flowers" resemble miniature dahlias, daisies or pinks, with "petals" symmetrically placed and beautifully colored in rose, blue, red, lavender, green, or pure white, according to the species. The "petals," however, are in reality mobile tentacles and constantly move about, contracting and expanding as they capture tiny invisible organisms and carry these to the central disc-like mouths.

The most interesting and surprising feature of the hydroids is the fact that each of the "flowers" on a stem is in reality a separate animal whose lifetime is occupied by carrying out some one single function and nothing else. One form of these living flowers may do nothing but eat; another that resembles an unopened bud may be the hydroid nursery; yet another may be designed to devote its life to building.

Moreover, many of the hydroids do not produce eggs or young hydroids as we might expect. Instead, when the fruitlike "buds" finally open, they release free-swimming jellyfish! If we should open one of the ripe buds we would find it filled with thin, slightly convex discs something like minute saucers, all attached to a common center. Finally, one at a time, these saucerlike objects detach themselves, and turning upside down, are instantly transformed into tiny jellyfish that swim away, with translucent bodies pulsing and miniature tentacles trailing behind them. It certainly is strange enough that a plantlike creature attached to rocks or other objects should give birth to the mobile jellyfish, but what follows is even more amazing. When fully grown, the hydroid-born jellyfish, or *medusae*, lay eggs that swim rapidly by means of minute hairs, called cilia. But they never grow up to become other jellyfish. Instead they settle on rocks or other solid objects, attach themselves securely and grow into plantlike hydroids.

There are, however, a great many species of these strange sea creatures that do not produce jellyfish but young hydroids, and there are also a great many kinds which do not lay eggs that become hydroids, but whose

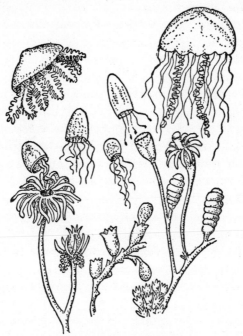

Hydroids and jellyfish

eggs hatch into young jellyfish. Most of the hydroids whose young are also hydroids are even more delicately beautiful than those whose offspring are jellyfish. Some creep and crawl about like vines, others have stiff, straight stems, others look like bunches of ostrich plumes, but the majority are covered with fine, fernlike foliage and hundreds of lovely, starlike "flowers."

Although most of these hydroids are small, many that live in fairly deep water reach a considerable growth, and sometimes after a gale or heavy seas, clusters of hydroids over a foot in height may be found washed up on the beaches. In Japanese waters there is a truly giant species living in deep water. The "flowers" of this magnificent creature are often four feet in length, their tentacles extending outward about the central disc for two feet or more. There is a Japanese legend which says these huge and beautiful creatures guard the secret undersea bower of a sea nymph.

The majority of the hydroids are soft and flexible, but there are many that are so hard and dense that an amateur biologist might easily mistake them for corals. One of these, commonly known as elkhorn coral, is abundant in the West Indies and on the Florida Keys. In life these millepores are covered with the fleshy animals of the hydroids and are pinkish, yellow, orange or brownish in color, but when cleaned and dried, as we see them in the shops and museums, they are snow-white. To the naked eye the surfaces of these coral-like hydroid growths appear perfectly smooth, but if we examine them under a lens we will find that the entire surface is thickly covered with tiny openings, or pores.

There are two different sizes of these pores; in life each is occupied by a single animal, the ones in the larger openings devoting themselves to eating food, while the mouthless animals in the smaller pores spend all their time capturing prey with their poisonous stinging tentacles and feeding their ever-hungry larger fellows, as well as protecting them from enemies. Each of the countless animals occupying the innumerable openings in a millepore is connected to all the others by the soft gelatinous tissue covering the entire surface, and each is a unit in the whole colony, where everything is shared in common.

The food consumed by the living mouths nourishes the entire colony, the food-capturing animals providing the food and in turn receiving their portion of the nourishment from it. The creatures who are destined to spend their lives at construction work, never worrying over being fed and protected, devote all their energies to making the coral-like structure a bigger and better home for themselves and their fellows.

Although a vast number of the hydroids are stationary, there are some that never take root, but constantly move about in the sea. A great many species of our larger jellyfish are in reality free-swimming colonies of hydroids supported by the body, or float. The best known and probably the most remarkable of these mobile hydroid colonies is the Portuguese man-of-war. It is a lovely creature familiar to all visitors of tropical and semi-tropical seas and shores; often during the summer it is carried northward as far as New England by the Gulf Stream. The creature's gleaming, bladderlike floats always attract attention as it drifts about on the surface of the sea, or is washed up on the beaches. Unfortunately the creature is as dangerous as it is lovely, for although the floats themselves are harmless, the long tentacles beneath them are provided with stinging organs so powerful that they will disable and even kill human beings. Even after the Portuguese man-of-war is dead and washed up on the beach, the stinging tentacles may cause serious injuries; each sting feels like that of a big and vicious hornet.

However, only a portion of the many tentacles are capable of stinging, for like other hydroid communities the Portuguese man-of-war is a congregation of numerous

individual animals, each with its allotted duties and all
joined together to form a composite entity. Thus some of
the tentacles do nothing but feel about, capture food and
serve as drags to prevent the man-of-war from drifting too
swiftly; other tentacles are lasso-like and bear the stinging
organs for driving off enemies. Close beneath the float
are other appendages that devour the food; still others, in
clusters like berries, produce the eggs. Certain of the organisms repair any injuries that may occur and constantly
increase the size of the entire colony; others are the sailors
who navigate this remarkable living ship. Strange as it
may seem, the Portuguese man-of-war does not drift hither
and thither at the will of winds, tides and currents; under
ordinary conditions it is sailed, steered and handled by special organisms and even makes headway against the wind
or may be made to remain motionless.

All this is accomplished by means of the shape of the
float and by the non-poisonous tentacles. If you examine the
float or "bladder" of one of these creatures, you will notice
that one end is much larger and more rounded than the
other and that a stiff comb or ridge extends lengthwise
from one extremity to the other. All of the numerous tentacles and other organisms are fastened to the larger, blunt
end of the float, with the longest tentacles on the outside.
Trailing through the sea, the tentacles serve as rudders
and keep the ridge or "sail" before the wind. If the little
living ship moves too swiftly, the tentacles extend themselves to greater length, thus offering more of a drag; if
more speed is desired, they contract, offering less resistance. When a change of course is wanted, the tentacles
change position, bunching together farther aft, thus pull-
ing the stern down and raising the bow to catch more
wind. The tentacles also serve as a centerboard to prevent
the ship from making leeway. And if the colony wishes

to remain motionless or come to anchor, the tentacles extend themselves to greater and greater length—sometimes as much as fifty feet—until the colony comes to rest.

Many persons who visit the Florida beaches or the West Indies mistake another remarkable floating sea creature for the Portuguese man-of-war. This is known as the *Velella* jellyfish and, like the man-of-war, it is a colony of hydroid animals supported by a rainbow-colored float. But instead of being shaped like a dirigible balloon, the *Velella's* float is broad and flat, dazzling blue with an iridescent sheen. Diagonally across this float there is a low, triangular fin or "sail" and the interior of the float is divided into watertight compartments that make it unsinkable. Beneath the float the *Velella* is very different from the man-of-war, for the tentacles are short and threadlike, extending only a short distance below the float. As in the Portuguese man-of-war, each form of tentacle has its specific duty. Some tentacles do nothing but eat; some capture the food; some can sting; others are feelers, or rudders.

Although the *Velella* is a very common creature, often cast up on the shore by thousands, the young are unknown. No scientist has yet found or seen a baby *Velella*, but in the same seas where this animal abounds there are two other strange jellyfish, one known as *Porpita*, which has no ridge or "sail" on its float, and another known as *Rataria*. The latter is supposed to be the young form of either *Porpita* or *Velella*, but so far no one can solve the puzzle.

As far as it is known, none of our jellyfish are edible, but in Japan certain kinds are highly prized as food. They are prepared or cured by a mixture of salt and alum or are tanned by means of astringent plant juices and may be kept indefinitely. Cut into strips, soaked in water, and properly cooked, they are very tasty and nourishing.

Nearly all jellyfish are phosphorescent, as are most other forms of hydroids; a large part of the phosphorescence in ocean water is caused by countless small jellyfish.

The largest jellyfish found on our coasts or in temperate seas are not over three feet in diameter, but in the Arctic seas there are giant species seven or eight feet across, with tentacles over one hundred and twenty-five feet in length. If these huge creatures emitted as much phosphorescence in proportion to their size as the tiny species along our shores, a single one would illuminate hundreds of cubic feet of water and would look like a submarine searchlight.

3

Flowers of the Sea

WHEREVER there is a tide pool or a rocky shore, you will find some species of sea anemones, the flowers of the sea. Many of these that live in northern seas and shallow water are quite beautiful, but those that are at home in deep tropical waters are far more lovely and much larger. Many are gorgeously colored giants, but large or small, dull-colored or brilliant as any flower on land, all are very similar in form. All have fleshy bodies, or stems, and numerous fleshy tentacles arranged like petals of flowers around a central disc. In every type there is a mouth-opening in the center of the disc. Several species have delicate, slender tentacles; others may have short stout ones, or countless small tentacles in multiple rows, like the petals of a double chrysanthemum.

The majority are firmly attached to rocks or other objects, but there are species that are free and swim about, and others that live with their bodies buried in the sand.

The sea anemones generally are a riot of color. Although some are dull olive or brown, with the tentacles paler or whitish, the greater number of these flowers of the sea are brightly colored. One species, common in tropi-

cal and sub-tropical seas, often having tentacles nearly two
feet in length, is olive-green with bright-green tentacles
tipped with vivid magenta or cerise.

Another large anemone of the West Indies and the Bermudas has an ivory-white body with innumerable long,
slender tentacles, which are rose pink. A closely related
species is even brighter red with a row of cobalt-blue,
eyelike spots. Some are orange, with tentacles ornamented
by alternating bands of deep red and pink, while others
may be delicate pink with bands of white on the tentacles.
In fact, there is no limit to the number and combinations
of colors; very frequently the same species may be one
color—or combination of colors—in one locality and totally different in another spot.

These flowers of the sea are beautiful but deadly, for
they possess "lasso threads" and powerful stinging organs
with which they seize and kill their prey or drive off enemies. If a foe is too large to be repelled by these weapons,
the anemone instantly pulls in its tentacles and shuts up
within its tough body like a drawstring bag. Sea flowers
look incapable of doing much damage with their stingers,
but even our small northern species can kill or stun a good-
sized minnow or a large shrimp, and many of the large
tropical anemones can inflict very painful and even dangerous injuries on human beings.

Although it is true that the majority of sea anemones
are attached to solid objects, they are not immovably fastened, as are oysters and barnacles. They adhere by means
of a hollow base that acts like a vacuum cup. These
anemones can alter their positions and move slowly from
place to place, but there is one group which is permanently
stuck to rocks, dead shells and other solid objects, or even
hard sand. Scientifically speaking, the *Zoanthus,* as it is
called, is not a true sea anemone, but the two are so simi-

lar in appearance and habits that only a trained zoologist can distinguish between them.

Unlike the independent animals of an anemone, the units of the *Zoanthus* are all connected by tissues that form a matlike growth. In color it varies from dull brown through orange to pale yellow; there are bright green and even vivid red species. Some of the *Zoanthus* camouflage themselves with bits of broken coral and other trash, so that they appear to be true corals. This habit is most in-

Sea anemones
1. *Free-swimming anemone*
2. *Zoanthus*

teresting, for the *Zoanthus* is a first cousin of the corals and forms a link between the corals and the sea anemones.

You may not see any resemblance between a big sea anemone and a coral, a sea fan, a sea rod or a sea feather, but if you examine a live coral you will find it very different from the dead, bleached specimens seen in museums and curio shops. Live corals are never white; usually they are gaudily colored. The so-called rose corals may be brilliant emerald-green, lilac, purplish-gray or a combination of all. The rounded star corals are invariably bright yellow or dull green; brain corals are vivid orange; staghorn or elkhorn corals are lilac, pink, or deep maroon, and other species are bright red.

All of these colors are in the soft, fleshy animal matter that covers the hard lime skeleton; in this mass there are numerous polyps or animals, each with a disc-like center, and a mouth surrounded by tentacles exactly like those of the sea anemones. Like the anemones, the coral animals can instantly retract, hiding themselves in apertures of the lime formation. If undisturbed and fully expanded they cover the surface like myriads of tiny flowers.

Gorgonian animals
1. *Sea rod and polyps*
2. *Sea whip and polyps*

In addition to the corals there is another group of sea creatures bearing animal matter very much like anemones. These are known as gorgonians, or Alcyonaria, and include the sea fans, sea rods, sea whips, sea feathers and sea pens, as well as the odd "organ-pipe" coral and the so-called "precious," or red coral. All of these gorgonians consist of a horny central stem which may be flexible or rigid. Covering this is a layer of skin consisting of flesh filled with innumerable tiny glasslike spicules; outside of this is a coating of gelatinous material bearing anemone-like polyps. Like the true corals, many of the gorgonians are bright-colored when alive, but—with the exception of the sea fans and some of the sea whips—they turn dark or dull-colored when dried and very often the fleshy covering drops off, leaving only the horny central stem.

When alive, the red coral bears no resemblance to the

polished beads or branches of red coral used for jewelry.
In life the outer surface of this gorgonian, rough and far
from attractive, is covered with white, flowerlike animals.
This coral, as we know it, is merely the central stem or
shaft, corresponding to the horny stalk of the sea rods and
similar gorgonians. Finally, there is the so-called "organ-
pipe" coral. This consists of a number of tubular cells,
each containing a green animal with long feathery tenta-

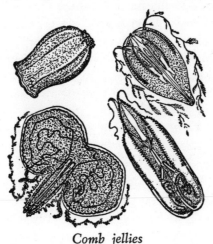

Comb jellies

cles. The tubes are separated by open spaces but are
connected by horizontal platforms, all covered with a vivid
red, fleshy material.

Certain species of sea anemones swim about by expanding and contracting their bodies, thus drawing in and forcing out water somewhat in the manner of a jet-propelled
craft. Far stranger and more remarkable than these mobile sea flowers is the sea creature known as Venus's-
girdle. It is quite common in tropical seas, especially in
the Mediterranean, and looks like a broad, undulating ribbon of iridescent silk. At night, looking like a band of

phosphorescent fire, it swims with graceful movements through the sea. Although when viewed from a distance this looks like a piece of ribbon some five or six feet in length, in reality it is much more complex. Equipped with eight swimming organs resembling combs, it also has an eye or sensitory organ, a mouth and two short tentacles. Outwardly it does not in any respect resemble a sea anemone, but scientists consider it a connecting link between the anemones and marine flatworms.

Another remarkable group of sea creatures are the animals known as comb jellies, so called because of their outward resemblance to ordinary jellyfish, except for the appendages known as comb-plates, which are arranged in eight rows on the outer surface of the animal. Each of these plates is hinged and has numerous hairs along the edges. They serve as oars or paddles, constantly beating the water in regular succession and, by breaking up light rays, they produce a beautiful display of rainbow hues traveling along the rows of combs. Quite frequently, though, they are carried into shallow water or cast up on our beaches by storms and, mistaken for stranded jellyfish, are ignored.

Even though many of the comb jellies resemble true jellyfish in general appearance, they can always be recognized by their method of swimming—using the combs, instead of moving by pulsations of the body as do ordinary jellyfish. There are many species of the comb jelly. Usually they are only a few inches in diameter, but the shape varies widely. Some are spherical; some are long and cylindrical; others have slender bodies with wide lobes like the wing of a butterfly. The jellies live in the open sea, mostly in the Gulf Stream, and since nearly all are highly luminous at night, the ocean sometimes seems to be on fire where the strange creatures abound.

4

The Island-Builders

As a rule, we think of corals as inhabitants of tropical seas, but there are many species found as far north as New England. These, usually small and inconspicuous, are attached to rocks in tide pools or on ledges; a few are deep-water species which are frequently washed up on our northern beaches. However, these northern corals do not build reefs and islands. Neither must we assume that all tropical corals are reef-builders, for many of them, like those of the north, live attached to objects far from the reefs.

In order to survive, those corals which do build reefs must have warm water—a temperature of 68°F. or more. Even in the tropics, water more than one hundred and fifty feet deep is too cold for them to thrive. Moreover, many species need air, and all need light. For that reason, these corals are rarely, if ever, found in water more than one hundred feet deep; many grow largest and most rapidly where they are close to the surface, left exposed by the tides or just barely awash.

The reefs are composed of many kinds of coral. Scores of species grow together, although certain kinds are restricted to definite depths. Hence there is a well-defined

25

stratification of the various species. Such massive types as the star and brain corals are found mainly at the bases of the reefs or a short distance above. The shelf, or mushroom, forms grow everywhere; the branched corals are at their best at and near the tops of the reefs. These madrepores—a group of corals that includes most of the reefbuilders—vary greatly in form according to the depth at which they grow. In the deeper water they may be covered with slender branches and long, needle-like twigs; near the surface they have a tendency to grow in broad palmate forms resembling moose antlers.

None of the corals actually construct the reefs, which are formed by accumulations of coral fragments, pulverized coral, dead sea shells and dead coral—the skeletons of the living polyps, all cemented together into a solid mass by the action of sea water on the lime of the corals. Neither is a coral reef a solid mass or wall rising from the floor of the sea. They are always riddled with openings, from small holes to huge caves. Very often such reefs consist of great columns or pillars, and when viewed from underwater look like temples or partially ruined buildings.

As the polyps increase in size and their lime skeletons become larger and larger, more and more die and are broken to bits, and all sorts of odds and ends become lodged upon the corals that are near the surface. Also, as the corals grow, the animals give off great quantities of carbon dioxide and ammonia, producing a reaction in the water near the corals. The lime in the water is precipitated in the form of calcium carbonate, or limestone, which rapidly crystallizes into hard rock. As the polyps are thus being encrusted with the cementlike material, they continually grow upward and outward, while behind and below them the limestone continues to increase. Although the amount of carbon dioxide and ammonia produced by

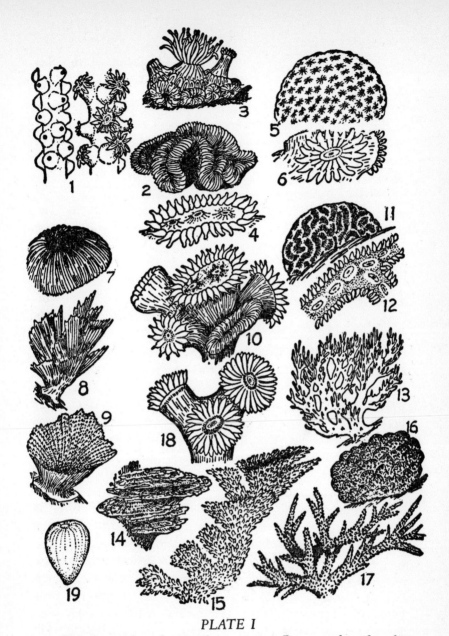

PLATE I

1. Branch coral and animals 2, 3, 4. Rose coral and polyps
5, 6. Star coral and animals 7. Mushroom coral 8, 9. Cup corals
10. Cup coral polyps 11. Brain coral 12. Polyps of brain coral
13. Lace coral 14. Shelf coral 15. Staghorn coral 16. Porite,
or lump coral 17. Buckhorn coral 18. Polyps of buckhorn coral
19. Larva of coral

any one coral is minute, the millions of animals that cover the reef produce an almost incredible quantity of the chemicals. So great is the aggregate of carbonate of lime thus formed that immense amounts are held in suspension in the sea water at long distances from the corals, eventually to be deposited as a calcareous coating on stones, sea shells, seaweed and other objects, so that they look like fossils and bear little resemblance to their original forms.

We must also bear in mind that all coral reefs have an underlying foundation of solid rock, for corals cannot grow on sand or mud. Whatever the shape of the rocks, the corals growing upon them build reefs that follow the rock-forms. Hence reefs rise in sheer cliffs, or are perpendicular on one side with a gradual slope on the other. Some may be broad and flat; others may be rounded. If the rock foundation is the rim of an extinct volcanic crater, the corals will form circular reefs known as atolls.

At varying distances from the shores of tropical lands and islands there is a fairly continuous line of submerged ridges, great boulders and other remains of the rocky land that in past ages sank beneath the sea. Here the light, shining through crystal-clear water, the warmth of the ocean near the land and the constant aeration of the sea by the backwash of the surf make an ideal environment for the coral growths which form the barrier reefs. Largest of all these is the Great Barrier Reef of Australia, which stretches for a distance of 1250 miles along the northeast coast of Queensland. The next largest barrier reef is the Bank of Campeche, which runs for several hundred miles off the eastern coast of Yucatán and southern Mexico.

The seas, breaking upon these reefs, cause the corals to grow more rapidly on the seaward side, while the fragments and masses broken off by the surf are carried over the reef and piled up on the leeward, or inshore, side. As a result, the reefs build up more quickly on this sheltered side. The more they grow, the more sheltered they become; more and more flotsam and jetsam lodge there and add to the accumulated mass.

In time, such a reef may extend shoreward until the lagoon between the original reef and the land is completely filled and the debris carried in by the waves rises above normal water level and becomes dry land. Soon vegetation appears on this new-formed island. Borne by the ocean wind, seeds of beans, sea grapes, grasses, sedges and palms lodge, take root and sprout; in a surprisingly short time the former lagoon becomes jungle-covered land fringed by waving palm trees.

Where corals have grown on the rim of an ancient submerged volcano, the same results follow: the coral atoll becomes an island, often a large one. Atolls, however, may be formed without volcanic craters for foundations. For example, the center of a reef may be gradually washed away by breaking waves; since the corals grow far more rapidly around the outer edges, the central depression becomes larger and larger as the old coral is washed away and dissolved by the chemicals in the water, whereas the surfaces exposed to the sea grow outward until an atoll is finally formed.

Other coral islands are the result of reefs having been elevated above the sea by volcanic upheavals. In the West Indies, one may find ancient coral reefs high in the mountains, thousands of feet above the present sea level.

In many places these uplifted reefs have been transformed into marble. In some areas the marble is composed of myriads of small corals and coral fragments; in other localities it is made of large corals, just as they once grew upon the reefs. Many of these coral marbles are attractively colored in gray, pink, brown or green, and when cut and polished are most beautiful, every detail of the coral's structure being clearly revealed. Finished pieces of these coral limestones serve as paperweights and other ornaments, and large slabs are sometimes used for table tops.

Finally, there is the class of coral island to which the Bermudas and most of the Bahamas belong. This type consists of "aeolian rock," which is composed of the fossilized remains of corals and sea shells which have been deposited by the wind, cemented to sand by the carbonate of lime dissolved by rainwater, and finally redeposited to form the "rock." As a rule, these islands are low, their highest points being not more than a hundred feet above the sea, but in some cases they have been lifted by subterranean forces to mountainous heights.

Another characteristic of this type is the abundance of caverns and grottoes. These are usually caused by loose pockets of sand and debris being washed out of the surrounding rock, but some are caverns that existed in the original reef. The latter are often immense and usually beautiful. Their ceilings are hung with countless stalactites; stalagmites rise from the floor; great sheets and folds of dripstone form columns and arches; everything gleams in soft tones of yellow, pink, red or crystalline white.

5

Worms Beautiful and Strange

ONE might suppose that there is little similarity between sea anemones and sea worms, but scientists consider the lovely Venus's-girdle a link between the two groups, a theory that is no more remarkable than the fact that many of the marine worms are fully as beautiful and colorful as any coral polyp or sea anemone.

Venus's-girdle

We always think of worms as ugly, slimy, uninteresting creatures of no value other than fish bait. As a rule, the only worm with which the average person is familiar is the earthworm, or angleworm, of our fields and gardens. Even the most ardent naturalist cannot deny that the earthworm and his cousins are far from attractive. When it comes to the worms of the sea, however, it is a very different matter; although some are similar to our angleworms in appearance, others are among the most beautiful forms of marine life, and even the unattractive kinds have strange and interesting habits.

If you have watched the life in a tide pool, you may have seen pretty, flowerlike growths rising from the sandy bottom, or waving above groups of small pebbles or empty sea shells, and assumed these were some species of sea anemone, or perhaps unusually attractive hydroids. The chances are that you never suspected that those groups of delicate, petal-like objects tinted with rainbow colors were sea worms, which closely resemble some of the sea anemones, but whose habits are very different. If you touch a sea anemone the creature at once retracts its tentacles and is transformed into a fleshy lump. But if you disturb one of the handsome sea worms, the flowerlike plumes will vanish, leaving no trace at all.

However, if you search carefully, without disturbing the sand or gravel, you may come upon some small holes; digging gently, you will find the burrow occupied by a most unusual sort of worm. Instead of being smooth and dull-colored like our earthworms, this creature's body is made up of numerous segments, each with a tuft of fine hairs and stiff bristle on either side. The entire creature is as iridescent as mother-of-pearl. Gleaming with dazzling emerald, green, golden yellow, crimson, purple and sky-blue, according to the way the light strikes it, the worm's body is covered with tiny scales that, like the throat feathers of a hummingbird, act like prisms to break up and reflect the sunlight.

There is no trace of the flowerlike gill-plumes—the breathing organs of the worms—but they are there, withdrawn from sight. The worms also have eyes, or at least light-sensitive nerve centers, so delicate they can detect a shadow falling upon the outspread gills, which then are instantly withdrawn. If you should examine the clusters of these plumes you would find numerous true tentacles hidden among them. These serve to capture the creatures on which the worms feed. In some species there is a long, tubelike proboscis in the center of the plumes, which is provided with sharp cutting teeth.

1. *Worm tube of sand*
2. *Worm tubes on rock*

Many of these plumed sea worms are satisfied to live in a hole in the sand with a thin coating of mucus holding the grains together; but other species build tunnels of lime for their homes. These slender white tubes—some straight, others crooked—may be found almost everywhere on rocks, sea shells and pebbles. In size the tunnels vary from tiny affairs no larger than thread to good-sized tubes a quarter of an inch in diameter and several inches long.

If you will gather some shells, pebbles and similar objects on which such tubes are present and place them in a dish of sea water, you will be surprised to see delicate and beautiful gill-flowers blossom from the ends of the tunnels. The majority are small and should be viewed through a magnifying glass to appreciate their beauty. One so closely resembles the garden pink that it is known as a sea dianthus; some look like miniature chrysanthemums; others are like full-blown roses; but no rose or pink on earth ever displayed such colors as these little sea worms.

Having watched and admired the little tunnel-builders, you will be interested in some other beautiful forms of sea worms. Often, when the tide goes out and the sand is left bare, you will find numbers of hollow objects jutting up from the beach like miniature corn stalks. These are the homes of the loveliest of all the sea worms—the pea-cock worms. As soon as the water again covers the tubes, great masses of long, featherlike gills appear as if by magic. Unlike the other sea worms' plumes, these are arranged in a fan-shape and decorated with eyelike spots and markings, giving the appearance of a peacock's tail.

Another group of sea worms make long transparent tubes with a number of doors that may be opened or closed. The worm not only lives in this apartment house, but carts it with him when he crawls about and hastily retreats within it and closes the doors behind him at the first sign of danger. Some sea worms make cornucopia-shaped tubes of sand cemented together. These are often found on beaches and mistaken for sea shells. Still other species of the marine worms construct complicated tunnels consisting of tubes that cross and recross one another to form a labyrinth that only the worms themselves understand.

And there are mound-builders, strange little creatures who build hillocks out of grains of sand cemented together, with an opening in the center like a miniature volcanic crater. The worms who occupy these mounds do not possess feathery gills; instead, their heads bear clusters of golden-yellow bristles that remind one of piano keys, and numerous whiskerlike white bristles on one side. The bristles are really quite remarkable, for they are covered with a sticky substance resembling birdlime and serving a similar purpose; it captures the tiny creatures on which the worms feed.

Many sea worms do not build their own homes. For example, one type which is white with brown stripes spends its life as the partner of a species of hermit crab. Making itself comfortable in the "attic" of the crab's shell, the worm is safe from all its foes. At mealtimes, however, the worm goes downstairs, slips unharmed between the crab's claws and jaws, and calmly helps itself to the latter's food. The crab, apparently, has no objection to the worm's shar-

Piano-key worm

ing its bed and board. Possibly he likes company; perhaps the worm renders him some unknown service. No one really knows.

Somewhat similar to the hermit-crab worm is a species that prefers a starfish as a partner. Despite the fact that it is a really sizable worm, over two inches in length, it makes itself at home in the grooves between the suckers on the undersurface of the sea star who, like the hermit crab, apparently does not object to being host to a worm.

Another group of worms very common in sand and under stones along our coast are the nereids. Six or more inches in length, they are handsome fellows, having jointed bodies gleaming with iridescent colors and bunches of bristles on each joint. Not only do these worms burrow in sand but they also swim freely and rapidly. The seemingly harmless bristles sting far worse than any nettles or bees; and these setae, as they are called, are equipped with minute barbs that remain under the skin and may cause sores or even small ulcers.

Somewhat similar to these stinging beauties, but differently shaped, are the sea worms commonly known as sea mice. Most of these are broad and flat, oval in shape, and about six inches in length. At the widest end is an inconspicuous head with two short tentacles. You would never guess that this creature is a worm, for it is completely covered with fine, hairlike bristles that throw off rainbow hues of iridescence. Although seldom seen, the sea mouse is quite common. It lives buried in sand or mud and hides under a little mound with which it conceals its handsome "fur." At times, however, heavy seas and gales wash hundreds of sea mice up on the beaches, where people often mistake them for some strange sea mammal.

The planarians bear a slight resemblance to the sea mice, although they are much flatter and bare of spines. These creatures do not look like worms at all; they are thin and flat and have crinkly edges, two short tentacles and two eyes. Normally they spend their lives crawling about on rocks and seaweed, although they can swim rapidly with graceful undulations of their crinkly edges. Many are whitish or flesh-colored; some are a brilliant red, orange, green, or a combination of several colors; others are mottled to match the surrounding sea growths so closely that the planarians are almost invisible.

At the other extreme of the sea-worm world are the fishline or bootlace worms. These are common and may be found beneath stones in shallow water. When undisturbed they appear more like little pieces of orange or yellow liver than like worms. But you will be more than

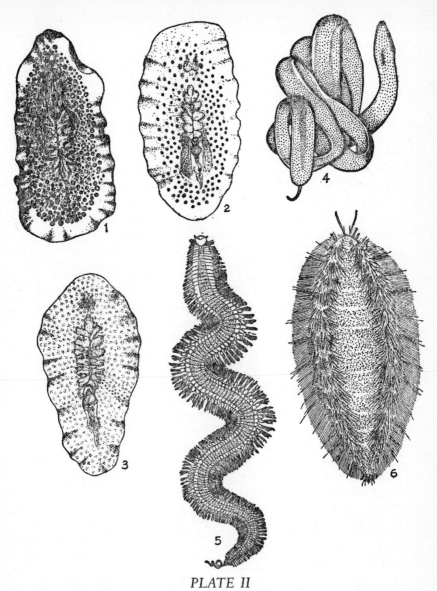

PLATE II

1, 2, 3. Flatworms, or *planarians*   4. Round worm, or *nemertean*
5. Annelid, or *jointed worm*   6. Sea mouse

amazed if you place one of these worms in a pail of water, for the creature will instantly expand and uncoil; very quickly he will transform himself into a whitish, fleshy worm as slender as a fishline and apparently endless. In fact, a fishline worm eighty or ninety feet long is not unusual. It is well named, for not only is it as long and thin as a fishline, but it is equipped with a "fishhook" mouth and preys upon fish. The worm's mouth is like a sucker; once it gets a grip on a fish it never lets go but "plays" its catch in much the same manner as a human fisherman, its extremely long body turning and twisting and offering so much resistance that the poor fish becomes exhausted and is devoured by its strange captor.

Few of us realize that some of the sea worms are important and highly prized food to certain peoples. One of these edible marine worms is the palolo, which is found in the waters about the South Pacific islands. The fact that the palolo is regarded as a rare food delicacy by the native islanders is not nearly as remarkable as the fact that these marine worms possess a most accurate and amazing sense of time.

During most of the year the worms live in holes and crevices in the coral reefs, where they are safe from their enemies, including man. But during October and November of every year, on the day before the moon is in its last quarter, the palolos suddenly appear in countless numbers. Emerging from their hidden homes in the coral, they swim up to the surface of the sea until the water is alive with millions of the creatures. But among the hordes filling the sea there is not a single whole worm. Each and every one is but the rear portion of the worm—the part that contains the eggs.

When the time for the vast uprising of the worms arrives, the creatures inhabiting the reefs wriggle their tail ends free; this portion, breaking off, swims to the surface, leaving the other part of the body, including the head, in the burrows. Palolos are highly colored; some deep green, others blue; some yellow, many scarlet; the sea appears to be transformed into a vast carpet of every imaginable hue. To the natives, however, the only beauty of the palolos lies in their gastronomic qualities. Knowing beforehand the exact date on which the worms will appear, the fishermen load their canoes with baskets and set out to sea. As soon as the palolos rise they are dipped up, the canoes filled and the loads paddled ashore, for the palolo does not keep when out of water but must be eaten almost as soon as caught. Thousands are devoured raw and thousands are cooked, the natives fairly gorging themselves.

Perhaps you may think that only dusky South Sea islanders would enjoy eating these sea worms, but the whites who reside on the islands where there is a palolo harvest are just as fond of the worms as are the natives. Even in the parts of California where these worms occur, people have found the palolos a real delicacy. What is considered edible and what not is all a matter of custom or habit. To the majority of people, worms, whether of the sea or of the land, are repugnant and hence unfit for food. Yet there is no reason whatever why sea worms, as well as many other marine creatures, should not be just as tasty and desirable as oysters or clams, whether eaten raw or cooked, or, for that matter, just as delicious as crabs, shrimp or lobsters.

6

Sea Squirts, Peaches and Puddings

No MATTER where you search along the shore, whether among rocks, in tide pools, under driftwood or on the piles of wharves and the abutments of docks, you will be certain to find the sea squirts, or ascidians. When they are disturbed, the sea squirts eject a stream of water, much like a bulb syringe will when squeezed. There are countless species known and I doubt if there is a stretch of shore two miles in length between Labrador and the West Indies where there are not at least a score of the species.

To be sure, the average person would never recognize some of these sea squirts as animals, for most of them look more like vegetables than animals. For that matter, even when you have learned to recognize certain forms of ascidians, you may—in fact, you probably will—fail to recognize others of the group, for there are few creatures varying so greatly in appearance.

Many of the ascidians are like masses of tapioca pudding; they cover rocks, shells and seaweed with a transparent coating. The color of the sea puddings varies greatly. Some are dull brown, others milky white; they may be red, yellow, green, blue, lilac, pink, orange or olive. When Victor Hugo wrote in his *Toilers of the Sea* that the walls of a cavern were splashed with crimson, as if giants had battled there, he referred to the blood-red ascidians that frequently cover rocks, especially in caves or grottoes along the shore.

Although at first sight these puddinglike growths appear to be lifeless things, if we examine them carefully we will find their surfaces covered with star-shaped dots. In some cases these are in regular rows; in others they form clusters or groups. In fact, they resemble miniature *Zoanthus* or some form of coral. Like the latter, the star-shaped dots are the true animals or zooids, corresponding to the coral and gorgonian polyps, while the puddinglike mass corresponds to the lime or horny body of corals and gorgonians. This is a superficial resemblance, for anatomically the ascidians are radically different from any other form of marine creature.

Unlike the corals and their kindred, the ascidian animals do not possess tentacles that can be expanded and retracted. Many, however, are very lovely; such, for example, is the Golden Star, whose animal matter is as bright and gleaming as polished gold, surrounded by a gelatinous mass of jade-green. Others may have zooids of white on a dark ground; the animals may be blue, royal purple, scarlet or orange. Some species of the sea puddings form large irregular lumps, six inches or more in height; still others may be raised on short stalks; but usually they follow the contours of the objects they cover.

All of these puddinglike forms are known as compound ascidians, for they are colonies of innumerable individual animals growing in a mass of the gelatinous material they produce. Not all of the common ascidians are permanently fixed; a number of species move about and even swim.

The latter are among the most interesting and strange of sea creatures and are known as salpas. There are two distinct forms which alternate with each generation. One of these forms is a single animal with two inch-long tentacle-like horns at the rear end. A number of buds soon appear on the creatures; these develop into little salpas that form double rows and produce a more or less cylindrical, transparent strip of tissue several feet in length. This strip contains hundreds of ascidian animals forming one colony, which swims about with a graceful, undulating motion. The transparent connecting material is tinted with pale rose and sky-blue with bands of white; salpas are indeed beautiful and sometimes are mistaken for the Venus's-girdle, described in Chapter 3.

Perhaps the strangest and most interesting peculiarity of these mobile compound salpas is that instead of subdividing or producing buds to produce more salpas, each animal of the colony lays an egg which hatches into the single animal form of salpa. This, in its turn, produces buds that become the compound colony form.

Although many of the ascidians belong to the compound class, there are numerous forms of the simple ascidians or true sea squirts. Apparently there is no limit to the form, color, size and location of these creatures. Many are spherical and resemble brightly colored "puffball" mushrooms. Others are so similar to sponges that they are frequently mistaken for them. Some are slender and tubular; others are branched; a number of species form irregular masses on the tips of tall, stiff stalks. As a rule the majority are brown, yellow, buff or red; but many are translucent or jellylike, and some are as transparent as plastic, revealing the animals' internal organs.

At the other extreme are species that are either as hard as stone or resemble stiff leather or rubber. Then there

are the ascidians known as "sea peaches," very common on
our Atlantic coast. Almost spherical in form, pink and yel-
lowish in color, and covered with a velvety, peachlike surface, they look much like their fruit namesakes. Instead
of a stem or blossom scar, the sea peaches have two short
nodules, each with a central opening; the moment the
creatures are disturbed they eject a stream of water, for
the sea peaches are true sea squirts.

There are also sea prunes, ascidians so wrinkled and
dark that their similarity to real prunes is even more striking than in the case of the sea peaches and their namesake.
Although the tubular openings in both of these ascidians are short and inconspicuous, other species have long,
attenuated tubes which make the squirts resemble carafes
or vases.

In colors these simple ascidians vary. Many are
whitish, others brown; some black. One of the commonest
species on wharf piles, shelly sand and rocks along our
coasts is brilliant orange. Almost equally common is a scarlet species, while others are emerald-green, lilac, crimson
or yellow. The most gaudy of all is a common species
whose oblong body is checkered with triangles of white
and rich purple.

Regardless of how greatly the ascidians may vary in
form, size and color, all are readily identified by certain
features. They all have more or less bottle-shaped bodies;
all have two openings, one for intaking water, the other
for ejecting it, and all will "squirt" when disturbed. As
the sea water drawn through the intake tube passes
through the animal's organs, all edible matter it contains is
digested and its oxygen absorbed. This is accomplished by
means of the ascidian's unique internal anatomy; the interior walls of the sac-like body are pierced by thousands
of minute openings forming a perfect sieve or filter. As the

indrawn water passes through the innumerable apertures, the most minute forms of life it contains are caught by the sievelike arrangement and pass into the sea squirt's digestive organs.

Although no one ever would suspect it, the ascidians possess a far more complex and highly developed anatomy than any other marine animal except fish, some of the mollusks, and a few crustaceans. They all have a heart that beats and pumps real blood through a complex vascular system. But unlike the steadily beating heart of the higher animals, the ascidian's heart pumps the blood in one direction for a given period, halts, and starts pumping in the other direction.

Of course there are very few creatures who do not have some sort of digestive organ, but in the majority of cases the stomachs of the sea creatures—other than fish, higher crustaceans and some of the mollusks—are little more than sacs. The ascidians have well-developed stomachs and livers and quite complex intestinal tracts. Thus these very lowly, vegetable-like creatures form a sort of connection between the invertebrate animals and the vertebrates insofar as their organic anatomy is concerned.

Still further linking them with the vertebrates is the even more astonishing fact that their young, instead of resembling the parents, are strange creatures which look like tadpoles, with well-defined eyes, brains, ears, mouths, a digestive tract, a complex nervous system, a heart, and, most of all, an embryonic backbone or notochord, somewhat like that of mammals such as man himself.

The strangest feature of these ascidians is that in their development they upset all of the accepted laws of nature; instead of the adults being more highly advanced than their young, they are more primitive. In due time the free-swimming fishlike larva, with its elementary spinal column, its eyes, brains, ears and mouth, its heart and its intricate nervous system, attaches itself to some convenient object and becomes a fixed ascidian. The notochord vanishes; there is a complete alteration of the nervous system; ears, eyes and mouth disappear, and all that remains of the internal anatomy is the digestive tract, the stomach and the respiratory and circulatory systems, which are totally different from those of the larval form. Why this should happen, why a creature well along on the road to the vertebrates should go backward instead of forward, thus upsetting the theory of evolution, is a puzzle no scientist can explain, a mystery of nature that no one has solved.

However, it is no greater mystery than the life history of one of the ascidians known as *Oikopleura,* or "housebuilder." Its larva, like that of the sea squirts, is a tadpole-like, free-swimming creature with a highly developed anatomy; unlike the other larval ascidians the *Oikopleura* refuses to obey the accepted rules of behavior and become a fixed sea squirt. Instead, it continues to swim about with its undulating tail, despite the fact that Mother Nature has decreed that the creature must become an ascidian and settle down.

It may not be able to ignore nature's decrees, but it manages to obey the letter of the law and yet have its own way. To do this the animal produces clusters of gelatinous ascidians, ofen larger than itself, that cover its body. Then, when its living cargo becomes too great and hinders its movement, the housebuilder throws off the accumulated mass and starts producing a new crop. Truly there are no stranger, more interesting and more puzzling sea creatures than the lowly ascidians; these squirts, puddings and peaches of the sea.

7

Sea Creatures We Use in Our Baths

DESPITE the fact that rubber and synthetic sponges have largely supplanted natural sponges, millions of true ones are still in daily use, for nothing can take the place of the natural sponge for many purposes. Although we usually think of them as bathing accessories, only a small portion are used in the bath. Many are used by physicians and surgeons, and thousands are used for washing automobiles, but the greatest number are used by glassworks, for natural sponges are the only known material that can be used for wiping off hot glass without burning or sticking.

Practically everyone is aware that sponges come from the sea, and that they are the skeletal remains of marine creatures, but few people would recognize a living sponge, for they bear little resemblance to those in daily use. When alive and growing, attached to some object beneath the sea, even the finest, softest varieties are rough, hard, slimy things, usually covered with broken shells and coral fragments and more or less filled with sand.

Moreover, there are hundreds of different kinds.

Some are spherical, some are soft, and others are almost
as hard as coral. Some grow in the form of hollow tubes
like candelabra; others are shaped like a vase. There are
sponges that resemble human hands, and sponges that
cover rocks, shells and other objects with a thin gelatinous
coating. Some are made up of countless interlacing stems
and branches; others are lovely things that seem to be

1. *Fig sponge*
2. *Vase sponge*

made of spun glass. In size they vary from tiny things no
larger than a pinhead to gigantic growths which weigh
hundreds of pounds and are several feet in both height
and diameter.

There is almost no limit to the colors of living sponges.
Some are dull brown or black, others are yellow, others
white; many are red, varying from deep maroon to the
most vivid scarlet; there are purple sponges, blue sponges,
green sponges, orange sponges and sponges that combine
several colors.

They are not confined to the tropical seas; many species are found along our northern shores and even in the Arctic seas. In fact you may find in practically every tide pool, rock, and shell a sponge of some sort, but such kinds have no commercial value since they are of no real use to man.

Many species of sponges are man's enemies, causing losses of thousands of dollars every year. These are the sponges that bore holes in oysters and other sea shells, and even in stones and concrete. It is almost impossible to find an oyster shell that is not riddled with holes bored by these sponges. As long as the holes are shallow and do not penetrate the shell they do no great harm, but if the holes are bored through the shells the oyster will die.

Moreover, sponges frequently form huge masses over oyster beds and smother the bivalves. Unlike that other enemy of the oysters, the starfish, the sponge enemies cannot be captured and destroyed by means of tangles or dredges, for they are as firmly attached as if they were a portion of the oysters' shells. In addition to the havoc they work on the oyster beds, they destroy stone and concrete walls, jetties and similar structures.

Among the species of our northern sponges are the mermaid's glove sponges, sometimes called "dead men's fingers." They have long tapering branches, pale buff in color and are so similar in form to a human hand that they are really startling. Another common sponge in our northern seas is the dainty little flask sponge that is shaped like a bottle and may be found attached to kelp and other seaweed. A number of common northern sponges closely resemble the fungi that grow on stumps and trees on land.

Regardless of their form, color, size or habitat, sponges are divided into two groups or sections, known as siliceous sponges and chitinous sponges. All sponges consist of a framework or skeleton composed of large numbers of spi-

cules. In the siliceous sponges these spicules are made of
silica and are hard and sharp like glass; whereas the skeleton or framework of the chitinous sponge is composed of
horny material known as chitin. This may be hard, coarse
and almost as solid as horn, or it may be as soft and fine as
silk. The bath and commercial sponges belong to this
latter group.

All sponges consist of many individual one-celled animals, the whole forming a colony bound together by the
spicular framework. In addition to the innumerable open-

1. *Boring sponge*
2. *Cup sponge*
3. *Finger sponge*

ings, each containing a sponge animal, there are countless
chambers, tunnels and canals within the sponge. Each of
these is lined with tiny, whiplike hairs which, when the
sponge is living, constantly vibrate and cause a current of
water to flow through the interior of the sponge. The
ever-moving water carries with it countless minute par-
ticles of food which are seized and devoured by the sponge
animals and, at the same time, provides the animals with
an abundance of the oxygen essential to them.

Although sponges produce eggs and free-swimming
young that wander about, finally to settle down and start
new colonies, they increase and grow by budding or cell
division. Each cell or animal constantly divides and forms

new cells. As a result, growth is very rapid, for even if a young sponge starts out with only one cell this may split into ten and each of these divide into ten more. Consequently, in a very short time the original baby sponge with its single cell will be a good-sized sponge with one hundred cells or more. Also, two separate sponges of the same species growing near together may unite to form a much larger mass; on the other hand, if a sponge is cut or torn into fragments each one of these will increase rapidly in size.

This peculiarity of the sponges has made it possible for the fishers to cultivate great beds and to obtain far better specimens than those growing naturally, for by placing clippings of live sponges on concrete slabs, very high grade, symmetrical sponges are produced. Moreover, it is not necessary to replant the sponge farm after the crop is gathered, for by cutting off the sponges instead of tearing them free, there is enough of the cellular material left to reproduce itself.

After the sponges have been gathered there is an immense amount of work to be done before they are ready for market. First the slimy, black animals, fresh from the sea, are placed in fenced-in areas of shoal water. Here the animal matter decays and is washed out of the skeletons. Then the sponges are carefully and thoroughly beaten, rinsed, and dried in the sun. But great care must be taken that they are not exposed to rain, for if, at this stage of their preparation, they are wet with fresh water, the chitinous spicules may rot and ruin the sponges.

If among sponges offered for sale you find some with rust-colored or orange spots on a vivid yellow surface, pass them by, for these have been ruined by rain and will go to pieces when used.

Fortunately for the dealers, the average tourist will select the brightly colored specimens and will pay a much higher price than for really fine sponges of dull buff or brown, so that an astute and wily sponge merchant often makes a larger profit from these culls than from the finest sponges in his stock. In some places in Florida and the West Indies some of the dealers place these rain-ruined sponges in cellophane wrappings with fancy labels, thereby obtaining fancy prices from gullible tourists.

When the crude sponges have finally been cleaned and cured they are trimmed by "clippers" armed with large shears, with which they quickly and most expertly cut off all irregularities, coarse edges and injured portions of the sponges. Considerably reduced in size by this process, but rounded and smooth, the sponges are then graded, assorted and placed on sale in the huge markets where they are auctioned off to the buyers.

Although the ordinary person could not judge the various grades, an experienced dealer or buyer is able to determine the quality and estimate the values at a glance. There is a great amount of difference in the quality of commercial sponges, which are usually divided into four varieties: "wire," "grass," "yellow" and "wool." The cheapest and commonest is the "wire" grade, used mainly for washing automobiles, store windows and the like. The "grass" sponges are used widely by glass manufacturers and are also the cheapest grade of bath sponge. The "yellows," not to be confused with the sponges yellowed by rain, are the next best grade of bath sponges, and the "wools" or "silks" are the finest and most valuable of all.

At one time sponging was one of the most important fishing industries in the world and was carried on in the Orient, the Mediterranean Sea, the Caribbean Sea and the Gulf of Mexico. But the invention of sponge substitutes so decreased the uses for sponges that the demand and values fell off, until today the only really important sponge fisheries are at Nassau in the Bahamas, at Key West, Florida, at Tarpon Springs, near Tampa, Florida, and in the Aegean Sea. The largest and most important of all the sponge industries is at Tarpon Springs, where it is not at all uncommon for the value of a day's sales to total over fifty thousand dollars, with annual sales of over one million dollars.

The majority of sponges fished, both at Tarpon Springs and in the Bahamas, are propagated on concrete tiles as already described. A few years ago some disease attacked the sponges and for a time it looked as if they might be completely wiped out, but sponges are pretty tough and the disease appears to have vanished. Also, many of the richest sponge beds were so depleted by overfishing that sponging scarcely paid. However, the enforcement of closed seasons on alternate areas for several years permitted the sponges to increase both in size and numbers. Then the discovery of artificial propagation revolutionized the industry and today there are more sponges, as well as more symmetrical and better-grade ones, than ever before.

Formerly all sponges were gathered either by naked divers or hooked up with long poles, a method that often tore and ruined the finest sponges. Although this type of sponging is still employed in the Bahamas, the spongers of Tarpon Springs use regular diving suits and are thus able to obtain sponges in water far too deep for either "skin divers" or hooking. Even the clippings have their uses. These and the poorest quality sponges are ground up and used in the manufacture of linoleum, sound-proofing materials, mattress and furniture stuffing and clothes padding; tons of the clippings are used as a ground conditioner and fertilizer.

The use of sponges dates back to the most remote times.

No one knows when human beings first learned to use sponges, but thousands of years ago the sponge fisheries of the eastern seas were very important. Sculptures, paintings and pottery of the Chimu and Muzo people of Peru found in ancient tombs at Chan Chan and elsewhere show the natives diving and gathering sponges.

Can you imagine using a sponge as a bathtub? There are certain kinds of the cup sponges that grow to such gigantic size that they would serve very well for the purpose. Often these immense sponges are five or six feet in

Venus's-flower-basket

height, fully as broad, and so hard and fine-grained that after drying they hold water almost as well as wooden tubs.

At the other extreme are the beautiful glass sponge and Venus's-flower-basket. The skeleton of the latter is an open network of long, glasslike spicules, forming a horn-shaped tube with graceful spiral ridges throughout its length. In the glass sponges the skeleton is small, cup-shaped and not at all attractive, but it is anchored in the sandy or muddy bottom of the sea by means of long, shimmering, glassy threads as fine as silk, composed of long flexible spicules, the whole having the appearance of a spun-glass tassel several feet in length.

Both the glass sponges and Venus's-flower-basket are inhabitants of the deep seas off Japan. Possibly they might be artificially propagated like ordinary bath sponges. If so it would be a most profitable industry, for these exceedingly beautiful sponges are highly prized by collectors and bring very high prices. As the clever Japanese were the first to cultivate pearls, they may devise a method of cultivating their valuable sponges and produce even bigger and better specimens than those fashioned by old Mother Nature herself.

Glass sponge

8

Creatures That Turn Inside Out

AMONG the strangest of sea creatures are the holothurians, usually known as sea cucumbers—since the majority of them resemble dull-green or brown cucumbers as much as anything else. They are common creatures found on sandy bottoms, in mud, under rocks and in tide pools. They range from a few inches to more than a foot in length, but all are somewhat alike: stouter in the middle than at the ends, rounded, and usually warty. Some are almost as firm as real cucumbers; others are soft and flabby, looking like nothing but bags of skin. However, the outward ugliness of the holothurian is deceptive.

If one is left undisturbed, or if it is placed in a jar of fresh sea water, it will surprise you by expanding and opening one end, from which numerous branching tentacles emerge. Slowly extending and spreading, they form a feathery mass, several inches in length and brightly colored. The sea cucumber now bears a flowerlike crown at one end, but more is yet to come. Slowly, from the warty surface of the body, innumerable stalked suckers appear as if by magic, and the entire creature begins to crawl, much in the manner of a starfish. This demonstration is really not so remarkable as it may seem, for the holothu-

rians are closely related to the starfish and other echinoderms, despite the extreme difference in their outward
appearances.

There are exceptions to the rule that sea cucumbers are
outwardly unattractive. One of the most beautiful sea
creatures found on the New England coast is a bright

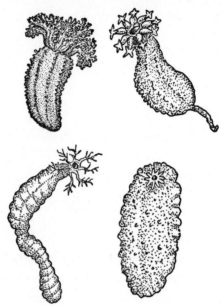

Holothurians, or sea cucumbers

vermilion holothurian about three inches in length with a
truly gorgeous crown of feathery tentacles.

Another species, which burrows in sand and is found all
the way from Cape Cod to Florida, is long, slender, and so
transparent that all of the internal organs are visible, provided the creature has not recently dined. When it has
had a full meal the body is a pale gray, because of the tiny
sea shells, pebbles and sand it has swallowed, which are
plainly visible. This odd creature grows to a length of

two feet and has a peculiar habit of dropping sections of its body from the rear end if it is disturbed or frightened. It may continue to break itself to pieces until only fragments remain, but it has not committed suicide, for, as in the case of its cousin, the starfish, the various sections will live and grow, and, in time, become whole holothurians.

The largest species found on our northern coast is often sixteen or eighteen inches in length when fully extended. Like all of the sea cucumbers, this big chap constantly changes its form and size, so that it may be as broad as it is long one minute and long and slender the next. Sometimes it is narrow in the middle and stout at both ends, like a dumbbell, or, in its contrary fashion, it may have slim ends and a bulge in the middle, like a snake that has swallowed an egg.

Another unusual type, known as the cotton spinner, is found in fairly deep water. This is a large dull-brown creature which, when disturbed, ejects innumerable sticky white threads so strong that they will capture and hold fast a large crab or a lobster.

All native holothurians are mere pygmies compared to some of the giants in the Arctic and tropical seas. In the waters of the Arctic and Antarctic regions, sea cucumbers five or six feet in length and thick as a man's thigh have been observed. They attain almost equal dimensions in the West Indies and on the Great Barrier Reef of Australia. This large holothurian not only makes its home among the corals, but actually feeds on them, managing to swallow good-sized pieces which are pulverized by the creature's internal organs. Then, after the coral polyp has been digested, the residual limestone is ejected.

Of all the strange habits of the holothurians, their most surprising trick is that of turning themselves inside out to escape a foe or to show their dislike of the surroundings.

Frighten a timid sea cucumber (a cowardly but instructive act) or place it in a dish of brackish water and watch its extraordinary gymnastics. First it writhes about, then its internal organs begin to protrude from the mouth; in a short time the intestines and other organs, as well as the feathery tentacles, will be completely free of the sac-like body. If it becomes calm, or is placed in fresh sea water, the versatile holothurian will survive; it will grow another body and replace its internal organs with new ones—truly a remarkable feat of total reconstruction!

Such a picture would not seem to generate an appetite for a meal of fresh holothurians, but many people regard them as delectable and nutritious food. Throughout the Orient—in the South Seas, Malaya, and especially in China, the big Pacific and Indian Ocean sea cucumbers are caught, prepared and marketed in large quantities. Under the name of *bêche-de-mer,* or "trepang," they are considered a valuable product of the sea as well as a most important article of trade. If they are dried in the sun and smoked for twenty-four hours, holothurians will keep indefinitely.

When first caught, sea cucumbers average about two feet in length, but by the time they are ready for market they have shrunk to the size of sausages. When boiled they gradually swell up to an immense size and look like masses of gelatine. According to the natives they are truly delicious. White men who have eaten trepang claim that it tastes like a mixture of smoked fish and glue. Apparently it is all a matter of taste and custom, but the *bêche-de-mer* is undoubtedly nourishing—just as all gelatine is nourishing. After all, why shouldn't gelatine made from the holothurians be just as good and as edible as our calves'-foot jelly, or our prepared gelatines made from hooves of cattle, or from the "innards" of sharks and other fish?

I have no doubt that many of the sea cucumbers found on our coasts are as edible and nourishing as the trepang of the Orient. A friend who is given to experimenting with new foods tells me that the large holothurians found on the Maine coast taste so much like lobster that no one would know the difference if he shut his eyes. Who knows but that some day "Sea-Cucumber Newburg," or "Holothurian Thermidor" may become one of our most costly and desired dishes? This is not at all impossible; a few years ago who would have dreamed that canned rattle-snake would ever become one of our most highly prized as well as highly priced viands?

9

Stars of the Sea

NEARLY everyone who has visited the seashore has seen the sea stars, or, as they are popularly
known, starfish. However, the latter name is a misnomer,
for the sea stars are no relation to fish, but belong to the
large group of marine animals known as Echinodermata.

Sea stars are found everywhere along the coast from the
far north to the tropical south, but few people who admire
their symmetrical beauty and their colors realize what
extraordinary habits these creatures possess. A dead sea
star, cast up on the beach, is usually shriveled and dull
brown, but on rocky shores or in tide pools, living specimens may be found which are very different-looking creatures of the sea.

Our most common species is usually purple or blue on
the upper surface and is covered with small, light-colored
tubercles; underneath, it varies from yellowish-white to
pale orange.

Sea stars normally have five arms, or rays, and when—
as sometimes happens—a person finds one with six or more
rays, he hails it as a real "find," a rarity like a four-leaf
clover. Actually, sea stars with excess rays are not at all
rare. Neither is it unusual to find one with only two or

three rays—or even one. Such sea stars are not freaks, like the six- or seven-armed individuals, but have merely lost some of their rays and are in the process of growing new ones.

Few creatures are as tenacious of life as are the sea stars, who are not only able to grow new rays to replace those that are lost, but will grow a brand-new body from a single amputated arm. Usually, if you carefully examine a starfish with less than five arms, you will probably find new arms budding from the edges of the old disc. As these become larger the tough little creature will have one or two full-sized arms and four or five shorter arms, giving it a strange, lopsided appearance. Sometimes when a five-armed individual has lost several of its arms, it may produce an extra arm or two in addition to those that are missing, for the creatures apparently are unable to distinguish the difference between a wound left by a broken ray and any other cut on the body. So, perhaps to be on the safe side, the starfish sends out a new arm from every injured spot on its body.

If the side or tip of an arm is cut, a new arm will sprout, so that occasionally we find sea stars with double-ended or even triple-ended rays. Even on our Atlantic coast there are many species of sea stars that normally have more than five arms. One very common species, known as the purple sun sea star, regularly has nine or more arms. It is less abundant than the common starfish and may readily be distinguished by its lilac or purple color, smoother surface and lack of the many conspicuous short spines.

Along the coasts of the western United States and South America are many species of the sun-ray sea stars, some normally having twenty-four or even forty or more rays and growing to immense size. In the harbor of Callao, Peru, I have observed sea stars three feet in diameter with

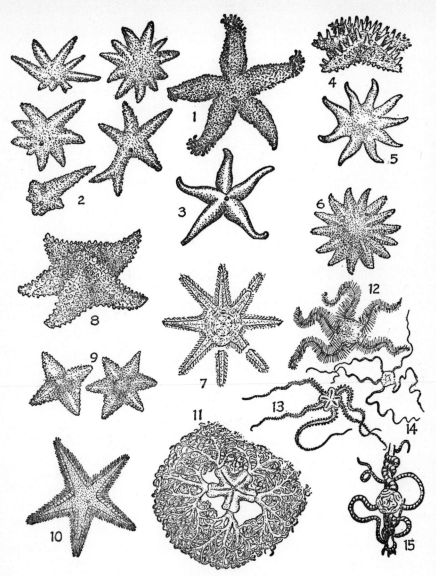

PLATE III

1. *Common sea star* 2. *Common sea star freaks* 3. *Common smooth sea star* 4. *Spiny sea star* 5. *Common nine-arm star* 6. *Sun sea star* 7. *Fragile sea star* 8. *Giant West Indian sea star* 9. *Giant sea star freaks* 10. *Gaudy sea star* 11. *Basket starfish* 12, 13, 14, 15. *Serpent, or brittle starfish*

over eighty short rays. Our own common species rarely becomes more than six or seven inches from ray-tip to ray-tip, and there is another fairly common species, vivid scarlet in color, which seldom grows larger than three inches.

All of these I have mentioned are shallow-water species, but in the deep water offshore are many other kinds, some of which are strange and curious-looking creatures. Along our more southerly coasts, from the Carolinas to the tropics, there are various kinds of sea stars. Some are five-armed species—when normal—and are far more symmetrical than those of our northerly shores. One highly colored species is a deep, vivid blue with brilliant golden-orange spines along the edges of the rays.

Perhaps the strangest of all is the brittle, or serpent star, prevalent in Florida waters. This is a large species; I have found many that were over three feet across. They normally have nine rays, sometimes more. When alive they burrow in the sand beneath the water, where they are completely concealed, although easily detected by the outlines of their arms in the sand covering them. They travel rapidly when disturbed, seeming to glide over the ocean floor, but their ordinary means of defense—or rather of evading an enemy—is to voluntarily break themselves into bits. Touch one or try to lift it; instantly the long, slender arms begin to drop off in sections, until within a few moments only the central disc remains.

For this reason it is almost impossible to preserve a perfect specimen. However, it can be accomplished, and out of hundreds I have managed to preserve and dry a few of the smaller sizes with all of the rays intact. As is the case with our northern sea stars, the central disc will put out new arms, and each of the self-amputated arms will eventually produce a new disc—provided some hungry fish or crab doesn't gobble it up.

Here in the same waters of Florida and the Bahamas there are myriads of the big West Indian sea stars that one sees dried, and sometimes dyed, on sale in curio and souvenir shops and roadside stands. In life these five-armed sea stars are orange, tawny brown or dull red in color, and when seen through the crystal-clear water they are very conspicuous against the sandy white bottom.

Now, having briefly mentioned a few of the more unusual and interesting species of sea stars of our coast, let's return to the shores of New England and the common everyday sea stars of our favorite haunts, the tide pools and rocky ledges. As we watch these sea stars crawling about among the seaweed, in sheltered cracks and crevices of the rocks, or in a limpid tide pool, they seem to be very harmless creatures, but they are a real enemy of man and an inexorable foe of the oyster fishermen. There is nothing a sea star loves more than a nice succulent oyster.

How on earth is it possible for a little sea star to eat an oyster, you may wonder? The creature has no powerful jaws or strong teeth, no large visible mouth; how can it dine on the hard-shelled bivalves? However, this dinner is a very simple matter for the sea star. It may not possess much strength, but what it lacks in power it makes up for in patience and perseverance; the sea star thoroughly believes in a tenacity of purpose. When hungry—and the sea star apparently is always hungry—it wraps its arms about an oyster, adheres firmly to the shell with its myriads of sucker-tipped tentacles on the undersides of the arms, and pulls steadily upon the two halves of the bivalve.

Tightly as an oyster or other bivalve shell may close, the muscles that contract to hold the shells shut are not tireless. Finally yielding to the strong, steady pull of the sea star's arms, the shell begins to open. Instantly the sea star squirts some of its digestive juices between the edges of the shell and pulls harder than ever. Stupefied by the contents of the sea star's stomach, the oyster shell opens and a most amazing thing occurs; the sea star actually turns its stomach inside out, encloses the oyster and proceeds to digest the animal of the bivalve. Finally, when the last fragment of the oyster has been consumed, the sea star pulls its stomach back within its body and crawls to another oyster to repeat the process.

Of course even a large number of sea stars on a big oyster bed, with its multitude of living shells, would do comparatively little damage, but instead of there being a few hundred sea stars preying on the oysters there are hundreds of thousands. As each of these ravenous creatures produces an astronomical number of eggs a year, we can realize what would happen to our oyster beds if even one egg in a thousand hatched. There would soon be no oysters, clams, or other shells left alive in the sea if all the young sea stars survived. Fortunately, infant mortality among sea stars is terrific; only a very small percentage of the young survive and reach maturity.

Even more fortunately for the fishermen and all lovers of these bivalves, the oysters are fully as prolific as their five-armed enemies. If all of the oysters' eggs hatched and all the baby oysters survived, there would be billions of new oysters in a single oyster family every year.

Still more impressive is the fact that four generations of oysters would produce enough shells to make a pile eight times as large as our earth. A single oyster spawns the incredible number of almost two million eggs, but only a small fraction of these reaches maturity. Whether the increase in the number of sea stars is greater than the increase of the oysters, or vice versa, no one knows. But every oyster-grower realizes that he must labor constantly—not in the hope of destroying these enemies, but just to keep them in check. Wiping them out completely would seem to be an impossibility, for there are millions of the creatures everywhere among the rocks and ledges; these constantly spread to the oyster beds, so that the task of protecting the beds from destruction is endless.

So far the only efficient means of capturing the pests is by using "tangles." These consist of chains covered with frayed-out rope fastened to a strong iron bar, which is provided with a yoke. As the rope-covered chains move over the oyster beds, the spines of the sea stars catch in the strands; the oysters, being firmly attached to the bottom, are not injured. Over the beds powerboats and good-sized oyster steamers move steadily back and forth, slowly towing their tangles, which, when drawn up, are usually covered with sea stars. Yet only a small proportion are destroyed in this way. For every one caught, scores escape, since the beds are rough, full of crevices and crannies which the tangles cannot reach. Moreover, it is impossible to cover every square foot on the surface of a big oyster bed.

Occasionally, after several days of thorough tangling, a bed may be practically free of sea stars, but more often there will be almost as many of the creatures on the bed a few hours after tangling than there were before. If anyone could discover a means of poisoning or otherwise eliminating the sea stars without harming the oysters, he would reap a quick fortune, but no one has come up with a complete solution to the problem as yet.

At one time the oyster-growers merely cut up the captured sea stars and tossed the fragments overboard, never realizing that in this way they were helping the creatures to increase; since each fragment produced a new sea star.

Nowadays the captured sea stars are taken to the shore and dumped on dry land or into fresh-water ponds.

Although living sea stars appear to be composed of solid meat or tissue, they have remarkable skeletons, barely held together by tough fibrous flesh and skin. In fact, their skeletal framework, internal anatomy, and their breathing and digestive arrangements are even more interesting and strange than their remarkable habits.

If we should remove the fleshy covering of a sea star, we would find it has a beautifully designed skeleton composed of calcareous plates. The exact form and arrangement of these plates vary with the species, but all are more or less alike. The upper surface consists of a row of fairly large plates arranged along each side of every ray, the spaces between being filled in with numerous smaller plates, usually more or less octagonal in form, and fitted together like tiles. On the underside there is a deep groove extending the length of each ray and bordered by fairly large plates with smaller plates between; in the center is the large opening of the creature's mouth. Regardless of whether the plates are large or small, they invariably form a perfect star with the same number of rays as there are arms to the creature.

In many species these symmetrically-placed plates form beautiful mosaic-like designs. In some species all the plates bear spines. In others they are spineless, but in all species of echinoderms there are innumerable spines in the integument that covers the skeleton. These spines are not rigid, but may be moved at will. Some are like tiny pincers and serve to keep the animal's surface clean by picking off any bits of foreign matter that lodge upon it; others, resembling the claws of a lobster, serve as weapons of defense.

If we examine the surface of one of these animals through a lens, we will find that the skin is riddled with minute holes. These are breathing openings; in life all these apertures will have minute, fingerlike papulae projecting from them. Somewhere near the center of the upper surface of the disc you will find a conspicuous, bright-colored spot consisting of a grooved plate. This is known as the madreporite and acts as a strainer through which the creature draws the sea water. Many people think this plate is the eye of the sea star, but the eyes are at the very tips of its arms—tiny spots surrounded by delicate, highly sensitive tentacles that are quite different from the innumerable stalked suckers lining the grooves in the rays. These suckers extend inward to the central opening, which has large, strong plates that serve as the creature's jaws. Do not be misled into thinking that a sea star cannot bite! If you carelessly place a fingertip within its jaws, it will nip you painfully and draw blood; some of the large tropical species can clip a good-sized bit of skin and flesh from one's finger.

You might search in vain for muscles in an echinoderm, for these strange and remarkable sea creatures depend almost wholly upon water power and are equipped with a perfect hydraulic pressure plant. This is known as their water-vascular system; it not only serves the creatures in place of muscles, but takes the place of the nervous system which the echinoderm lacks. In the center of the animal there is a "ring-canal" completely encircling the mouth. From this, the "stone canal" branches off between two of the arms and ends in the sievelike madreporite. Finally, within each of the arms, there is a connecting tube extending the length of the arm. These are known as "radial canals," which are small bulblike ampullae, each connected to the hollow tubes of the sucker-feet.

Throughout their entire lengths, these canals are lined with fine but powerful cilia that constantly beat inward, thus ceaselessly drawing in a constant current of water that keeps the canals and the tube-stalks of the feet filled with the fluid. By means of constructive tissue that might perhaps be considered muscle, the tiny ampullae are squeezed, forcing the water within the tubes into the adjoining feet, thus causing them to extend. Then, when the pressure is released, the water returns to the bulbs and the next tube-feet are shortened. Due to the fact that each tube-foot is equipped with an individual sense organ, the movement of the sucker-feet is under perfect control.

At the extremity of each of the feet there is a sucker disc that operates by vacuum and will adhere firmly to any surface. When the tube-foot is extended, the disc is pressed and flattened against the object it touches, the internal water pressure causing it to adhere. As hundreds of these sucker-tipped feet act together, alternately adhering as their tubular stalks are filled and releasing as the water is forced out, the creature can move quite rapidly. It operates its feet in alternating waves, taking hold in one spot, drawing itself forward, then taking a grip with the feet in front and releasing the others. By changing the motion of the feet from right to left, or from forward to backward, the animal can move in any direction. Seeming to glide rather than walk, it moves like a caterpillar-tread tractor. Once we understand the *modus operandi* of the sea stars' sucker-feet we can more readily understand how these creatures can exert a steady, untiring pull on the shells of oysters, for the suckers, operated by water, never tire.

Quite unlike the ordinary sea stars are the related creatures known as serpent starfish, spider starfish, brittle starfish, and basket starfish; these form the group known as

ophiuroids. All are characterized by having small central
discs and long, slender, flexible arms. In some species
having discs barely an inch in diameter, the arms may be
over a foot in length. In the species known as the serpent
stars the rays may be smooth and almost circular in
sections. In others the arms may range from smooth
to knobby. The spider starfish have arms bearing long,
closely-spaced spines.

Although many of these ophiuroids are quite tough and
may be picked up and handled or preserved in alcohol
without being broken, others are as fragile as the brittle
sea stars already described, and will drop off their long
slender arms on the slightest provocation. As these self-
amputated arms continue to live and squirm and writhe
about, they have all the appearance of some strange worm
or small sea snake. Most of these long-armed ophiuroids
live under rocks, in the sand, in crevices of coral or in
sponges and other sea growths, and some are so perfectly
camouflaged in coloration that it is almost impossible to
detect them until they move.

Finally, there is the strange basket starfish with its
small five-lobed central disc surrounded by a perfect labyrinth of branching arms, each branch dividing and subdividing until there are hundreds of them. In life these
strange creatures move about over corals and other sea
growths and manage their multiplicity of arms as easily
as the common sea stars handle their five simple rays.
But when killed or preserved, the countless branches of
the arms contract, curl inward and make a basketlike form
with the body disc in the center.

Anatomically all of these ophiuroids differ greatly from
the true sea stars or starfish. Instead of being more or less
rigid the arms are jointed and flexible; they do not contain
an extension of the digestive tract and there is no groove

or channel along their lower surfaces. They do not possess an intestinal tract; their digestive apparatus consists of a sac-like stomach connected with the mouth, which is equipped with five teeth, one corresponding to each arm. The teeth are sharp-pointed plates, with their tips turned inward. Back of these are a series of other plates, often forming a very regular and attractive pattern. Instead of having sucker-feet along the arms, these creatures have a few of the feet on the disc at the bases of the arms.

Neither is the body disc overlaid with a covering of integument; it consists of closely fitted, tile-like plates. Within the plate-covered arms there are a number of short sections of calcareous matter resembling vertebrae, but so formed and arranged that the arms are capable of movement only in certain directions. Instead of moving about by means of sucker-feet on their arms the ophiuroids rely mainly upon their snakelike arms to move about; they do so with surprising agility and speed, the sucker-feet near the bases of the arms and in the vicinity of the mouth being used mainly for attaching their disc to some object or for holding their prey.

Although the ophiuroids are largest and most numerous in the more southerly waters, a number of species are quite common along our northern shores and a few will almost always be hidden among algae, or under rocks or dead shells in almost any tide pool.

10

Dollars and Doughnuts of the Sea

AMONG the most abundant of sea creatures
along our shores are the sea urchins—spiny little fellows
who snuggle among the rocks or in shady corners of tide
pools, and whose skeletons, minus the spines and bleached
white, are washed up on the beaches. Outwardly there
seems to be no resemblance between a sea urchin and a
sea star, but they are first cousins. Both are echinoderms
and both have the internal hydraulic arrangement I have
already described. About the only real difference between
the two is that the urchins have longer spines than the
stars, are spherical in form, and have no arms.

If we scrape the spines from a sea urchin, or if we examine one of the denuded, bleached specimens, we will
find the symmetrical starlike pattern of the sea stars plainly
marked by lines of tiny openings on the urchin's back. On
the underside we will find a mouth-opening surrounded
by plates, very much as found in the sea stars. Like the
stars, they possess sucker-feet with which they move
about. In life, however, these details are completely concealed by innumerable spines, which may be short and
slender, stout and blunt, or exceedingly long. Each of

the spines is provided with a regular ball-and-socket joint
which permits it to be moved in any direction.

In addition to all these spines and the hundreds of
tubular sucker-feet, the urchins are equipped with a be-
wildering array of appendages or "tools," which may be
pushed out from their holes or withdrawn at the will of
the urchin. Some of these tools are perfect tweezers, others
are blades, some are viselike; many have slender, flexible
stems. There are flexible instruments terminating in triple
jaws with razor-sharp teeth, and tools that are brushlike,
covered with short stiff hairs.

Each and every one of these little appendages has its
own special purpose. No complicated, man-made machine
is more amazing than a sea urchin in life and action. The
mobile spines swing back and forth, first in one direction
then another, forming a defensive barrier against possible
enemies, or spreading apart to allow some small creatures
to come within reach of the numerous pincer organs that
will instantly grasp the potential meal and rapidly pass it
from one pincer to another until it reaches the mouth.
In the meantime the forceplike appendages are ceaselessly
picking off dirt and any foreign matter that lodges on the
creature's surface, while the little brushes sweep and scour,
and the blunt-tipped appendages, which have poison
glands, sway back and forth, in and out, ready to sting and
stupefy possible prey or to drive off foes.

If a fragment of fish or some other food is dropped upon
a living sea urchin a strange scene follows. Instantane-
ously, dozens of tiny pincer-claws grasp the morsel and
pass it quickly to the mouth on the underside, where certain other appendages taste and examine the tidbit to determine if it is edible. Once the material has passed the
test it is thrust into the opening, where five toothlike plates
grind and chew it to a pulp.

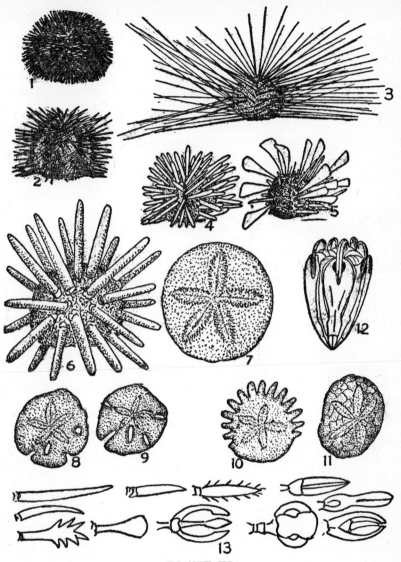

PLATE IV

1. *Common sea urchin* 2. *Boring sea urchin* 3. *Poisonous sea urchin* 4. *Blunt-spined sea urchin* 5. *Paddle-spined sea urchin* 6. *Club-spined sea urchin* 7. *Sand dollar* 8, 9. *Keyhole urchins* 10. *Cut-edge urchin* 11. *Sea beaver with spines removed* 12. *Aristotle's lantern* 13. *Sea urchin's "tool kit"*

The jaws may appear very simple affairs compared to the multitude of seemingly intelligent appendages, but they are one of the most amazing features of the urchins and are made up of forty distinct interlocked parts provided with connecting rods and toggles. No mechanical device operates with greater precision or possesses greater crushing power for its size than "Aristotle's lantern," as the urchin's masticating machine is called.

Quite apart from the anatomical wonders of the sea urchins, but almost as strange and interesting, are their habits. Although the majority of species are content to hide themselves in rock crevices and among seaweeds, other species conceal themselves beneath bits of broken shells held in place by their clinging appendages. Most people, thinking them merely accumulations of broken shells, would pass them by without a second glance—unless the apparently inert mass began to move along the bottom of the water.

Far more remarkable are the urchins who dwell in holes in rocks, for, incredible as it may seem, the holes are bored by the sea urchins themselves. No scientist has yet been able to explain how these echinoderms can drill holes in hard rock, for they possess no boring organs and their hardest spines and jaw-plates are softer than the softest stone. The urchins must be able to tunnel into the rock when very small; frequently we will find the tunnels occupied by large urchins where the openings to their rocky lairs are less than an inch in diameter.

It is possible that the echinoderms possess some fluid or chemical substance that softens or dissolves the rock, but if so, no one has yet discovered its presence. The tunnels are not restricted to any one kind of stone; they are as numerous in the hard igneous rocks of the Antilles as in the soft limestones of the Bermudas. Regardless of how it is accomplished, the feat of drilling into stone must be both simple and rapid for the urchins; in many localities the rocks and boulders along the shores are riddled with hundreds of holes which house echinoderms ranging from little chaps an inch or so in diameter to oldsters four or five inches across. Moreover, the young urchins may have tunnels much deeper than those of the adults. When housed in rocks which are constantly swept by waves and surf, each individual will occupy a hollow bored in the stone where it is protected· from the washing of the seas.

If man could solve the mystery of how the urchins bore rocks, and duplicate the process on a large scale, what a simple matter it would be to bore our tunnels through mountains and beneath rivers without having to employ costly and complicated machinery, plus the power of steam, electricity, compressed air and the other equipment now required!

The majority of sea urchins are harmless creatures and may be handled with impunity, but there is one species— all too abundant in Florida and West Indian waters—that is really dangerous. These are big black creatures with enormously long, slender spines that are as sharp as needles and will penetrate one's flesh at a touch and break off, leaving parts of the spines in the wound. Since they are provided with minute barbs, it is impossible to extract them, and a coating of poisonous slime on the spines makes the wounds become seriously inflamed and fester very quickly.

Fortunately there is a simple way to remove the bits of spines. By bathing the wounded areas in strong vinegar or a weak solution of muriatic acid, the calcareous spines are quickly dissolved and the poisonous material is neutralized. When collecting shells among corals or rocks where these big, poisonous urchins live, I invariably carry a bottle of acid with me; many a time it has saved me from serious results when I have accidentally stepped into a cluster of the long-spined urchins.

At the very opposite extreme in the way of spines are the big tropical sea urchins with spines from half an inch to an inch or more in diameter. In Hawaii, for example, where these club-spined urchins are found, their spines are used as crayons and slate pencils; in some ways they are far superior to chalk. There are species of sea urchins with flat, paddle-shaped spines, and others whose spines are covered with short branches or supplementary spines.

Quite different from the spherical urchins are the odd sea biscuits, sea doughnuts or sea beavers, as they are variously called. These are really a group of sea urchins that are oval in outline and have high, humped backs. They are completely covered with short, delicate spines that give creatures the appearance of being covered with hair or fur, and as they move about beneath the water they might easily be mistaken for some strange form of mammal.

One species quite common in Florida waters has very coarse "hair" and closely resembles a coconut half-buried in the sand. Most of these sea doughnuts are so well camouflaged in life that they are seldom seen and are considered quite rare. But wherever they occur you will find numbers of their bleached skeletons cast up on the beach. These, like the skeletons of the everyday urchins, have a perfect star formed of minute slits on the upper surface and surrounded by mosaic-like plates.

Other very common echinoderms found cast up by the waves are the sand dollars. Although these seem very different from the spherical sea urchins and the humpbacked sea doughnuts, they are really only a flattened form of the same group with the same internal anatomy and the same perfect star-shaped pattern of apertures on the upper sur-

face. In life, too, they are covered with small short spines
and are equipped with the same assortment of pincers,
tweezers, brushes and other appendages as the true urchins. Some of the sand dollars are almost perfectly circular with very thin discs; others may be higher in the
center than at the edges; some are irregular in outline,
while the species known as "keyhole sand dollars" have
perforations at or near the outer circumference.

Unlike the urchins, who prefer rocky lairs, the sand
dollars dwell in the sand, where they are quite invisible.
But when they move they always betray their presence
by leaving a well-marked trail behind them. To be sure, if
they travel along beneath the sand where there is water
or where waves lap on the beach, their trails will be wiped
out almost as fast as they are made. But in many places
where there is a tidal rise and fall of several feet, the sand
dollars burrow in the damp sand far from the edge of the
sea at low tide.

Once, while in Panama, I noticed numerous strange
markings on a sandy area many yards from the edge of the
water. They varied in width from four to eight inches,
and resembled miniature roadways or the impressions left
by a wheelbarrow passing over the sand. Some were as
straight as any motor highway, others extended in graceful curves, still others followed an erratic zigzag course and
quite frequently they crossed one another. But their most
puzzling feature was that they began and ended abruptly,
as if they had been formed by some object that had fallen
from above and, having made the tracks, had taken flight.
The puzzle was solved when, as I was studying the strange
little roadways, the track began to lengthen. No form of
life was visible, but yet as I watched, the trail moved
slowly onward. Quickly I scraped away the sand to reveal
a big brown sand dollar.

Interesting and strange as are all these various echinoderms I have described, none are more unusual than the group known as crinoids, or sea lilies. In appearance these creatures are far more like flowers than animals, although they are close relatives of the sea stars. Outward appearances are often most deceptive and if you should examine a crinoid carefully you would find that it is not so very different from a basket starfish. There is the same central disc with the mouth in the middle and the same five arms.

1, 2. Sea lilies
3. Feather star

At a short distance from the base, each arm is divided so that there are ten, all edged with delicate, feathery, flexible little spines.

The crinoid, however, is like an upside-down sea star, for its mouth is on the upper surface of the body. This is necessary because the crinoids, unlike all other echinoderms, are provided with stalks that grow from the center of the creature's back. Sprouting from the stalk are a number of flexible tentacles that resemble leaves, and at the base is a fibrous mass of roots by which the creature attaches itself to some rock or other object.

Like the other members of the echinoderm family, sea lilies are carnivorous, but since they cannot crawl about like the sea urchins and the sea stars to search for prey, they draw the food to themselves. Along the grooves in the arms are long, slender hairs that are constantly in motion, thus producing a current of water flowing toward the mouth, carrying with it the tiny animals on which the crinoid feeds.

Although the crinoids are all provided with stalks, some species, known as feather stars, do not remain fixed. When these reach a certain size, the lilylike "flower," or animal, breaks away from the stem and swims off, using its arms for paddles. However, the free-swimming creature is not forced to spend all its time moving about. Very soon little appendages bud out from the area where the stem joins the body and serve as grapples to anchor the creature to some convenient object. Sometimes the feather star may remain stationary for a long period; but it may settle down for only a short time and then flit about, alternately resting and swimming, like a marine butterfly.

Feather stars may be rose, lilac, pale orange, or pink. Although the majority of the crinoids are deep-water dwellers, there is a lovely rose or cerise-colored feather star not at all uncommon on the southern shores of England. Sometimes the rosy feather stars gather in great numbers in one spot and give the effect of a great bed of pink flowers beneath the surface of the water. The long-stalked true sea lilies, however, are usually pure white and never are found in shallow water. Some species inhabit the extreme depths of the ocean, thousands of fathoms beneath the surface.

The echinoderms are among the most ancient of all forms of life on earth. The crinoids were the ancestors of the sea stars, the sea urchins, the sand dollars, and the rest of that group. Like many another form of life, the present-day crinoids are microscopic compared to their ancestors of millions of years ago, which are preserved in the form of fossils. In those far-distant times the crinoids were exceedingly numerous; they were gigantic creatures with feathery tops as large as our palm trees, supported by stalks twenty feet or more in height. A forest of such huge creatures, their multicolored, featherlike arms waving gently back and forth, must have been a magnificent sight had anyone been there to see them as their tentacles curled and clutched at huge fish and passed them into the enormous, gaping mouths.

Just why the crinoids should have diminished so greatly in size during the millions of years that have passed since their heyday is a mystery. Surely there must be as much food in the sea today as in those immeasurably distant times, and we would logically think that the larger the creatures, the less they would suffer from enemies. And what other creatures would find the crinoids and echinoderms tasty food? It is true that some species of fish do devour sea urchins and that they are even considered good food by some human beings. In the West Indies, where the urchins are called "sea eggs," they are regarded as delectable, and are caught and filled with roe and eaten by the thousands. But I doubt if anyone could consider sea stars or crinoids as food—even if he were cast away on a desert island!

11

Sea Arrows and Lamp Shells

AMONG the strangest of all sea creatures are the remarkable animals that scientists know as the Chaetognatha, more commonly called sea arrows. A most appropriate name it is, for these little creatures—rarely over two inches in length—look strikingly like arrows as they dart about in the sea. Although they are always plentiful, at certain seasons of the year—and even at certain hours of the day—they suddenly appear in greatly increased numbers and form solid masses of sea life. Their presence may always be known by the flocks of sea birds hovering in the air, constantly darting down to seize a mouthful of them, while fish of all sizes and kinds, accompanied by porpoises—and even whales—gorge themselves on the swarming multitudes.

On one occasion, while sailing off the Pacific coast of Panama, my attention was attracted to great flocks of terns, gannets, cormorants, gulls, pelicans, and other sea birds hovering over the sea some distance away, while schools of porpoises, a number of small whales, and even several giant mantas—or devilfish—leaped, dived, and swam about. Wondering what had attracted so many hungry sea creatures, I shifted my course.

In a few moments I came upon a large group of spotted sea snakes—true, venomous reptiles. Each moment these pelagic serpents increased in number, and I discovered that they were feeding ravenously upon countless sea arrows. The nearer I approached the flock of birds, the leaping fish, and the porpoises, the more numerous were the snakes and their prey, until the clear blue water was gray and murky with millions of the swarming sea arrows and alive with writhing snakes. The birds and cetaceans were so intent on their prey they paid no heed to my presence, and I discovered that the birds were feeding on the sea snakes as the porpoises, whales, and mantas gobbled up snakes and sea arrows together.

However, I didn't stay to watch the fascinating sight for many minutes, since the wriggling snakes—many of them four or five feet in length—were constantly trying to climb into my boat. On every side there were hundreds of the sea snakes; as fast as I drove them from one spot, they came at another. Of course it was almost impossible for them to clamber up the sides of my craft, but again and again they managed to wriggle up the rudder or the bobstay, and despite my efforts and those of my companion a few of the reptiles did succeed in boarding us. Several times at sea I have witnessed the swarming of the sea arrows with their attendant birds and porpoises, but never have I seen anything to equal that unforgettable scene off the coast of Panama.

Almost anyone except a scientist would mistake the sea arrows for fish, since they have fishlike fins and fishlike tails. But the fins, unlike those of fish, are placed laterally and merely serve as balancing planes; the creatures swim by rapid vibrations of their semi-transparent bodies. Like fish, the arrows have a head as well as a body. The head has a vertical, slitlike mouth, and in some species there is a hoodlike fold of skin covering the dome of the head, and two rows of small teeth, as well as a row of long, sharp prehensile hooks which may be opened or closed over the sea arrow's mouth.

Despite their general "fishy" appearance, the sea arrows are not vertebrates. They are much further removed from the vertebrates than the young ascidians previously described, for they do not possess the least trace of a spinal cord. Anatomically they are one of the simplest creatures, with a digestive system consisting of a straight tube without a stomach and dividing the interior of the body into

Sea arrow

two sections. Since there are three main cavities in the creature's body, the resulting six compartments form what is known as a "coelom" in exactly the same manner that the peritoneal is formed in the vertebrates.

Although the sea arrow has a brain—or rather a ganglion—in its head, as well as optic nerves and a rather rudimentary nervous system, it has neither respiratory nor circulatory systems. In short, it is one of the most baffling and contradictory forms of life, being in some respects among the most rudimentary of living things, but in other ways approaching the groups leading to the vertebrates.

In their habits, the sea arrows are also paradoxical. They are carnivorous, feeding on all sorts of smaller fry, including larval fishes and crustaceans. They also devour one another without discrimination. As a rule, marine animals inhabiting the deeper portions of the sea cannot exist at or near the surface, whereas surface creatures cannot live in the great depths, where the pressures are terrific. But the sea arrows are exceptions to all rules and are as numerous at the greatest depths ever measured by man as they are at the surface of the sea throughout the oceans of the world. Since the sea arrows do not rightly belong to any other class of marine life, the scientists have made them a separate group, called arrow worms, which falls categorically between the squids and the echinoderms.

Almost as puzzling as far as their status in the zoological world is concerned, and almost as strange in many other ways, are the sea creatures known to the scientists as the

Brachiopods

Brachiopoda, commonly called lamp shells. In outward appearance these odd creatures look so much like sea shells that they were formerly considered mollusks, and even at the present time many conchologists collect the lantern shells as well as true sea shells. The name "lantern shells" was given these creatures because the hard calcareous shells of many species in the class are similar in form to the old Grecian and Roman lamps; on the other hand, there are many brachiopods whose shells have no resemblance to lamps of any kind.

According to the naturalists, the lamp shells are more closely related to the worms than to the mollusks, but since the group has some affinities with the bryozoans, they have been honored by being placed in a class by themselves. Today there are only one hundred and twenty species known, but in the far-distant past there were countless species inhabiting the ancient seas; more than 2500 species have been found in the form of fossils. The brachiopods are a very old form of life, for they abounded during the Cambrian period of the Paleozoic era, millions of years ago, and have survived practically unchanged, in both structure and appearance.

They are quite common in shallow water in many localities, although far more numerous in the deeper seas. If, on your ramblings along the shore in search for strange forms of marine life, you find some rusty-red or chestnut-brown shells attached to the ocean bottom by a short stem or stalk, you may be fairly sure you have discovered some species of lamp shell. Examining the shells, you will find a small hole near the apex of the lower shell; through this opening the odd creature thrusts its strong anchor-stalk.

The majority of the lamp shells are of this type, but there are others you would scarcely recognize as brachiopods. These have narrow, oval shells and are supported on long, slim, flexible stems extending deeply into sand or mud, where they are held by an anchorlike mass of sand grains cemented together to form a secure mooring.

Internally, the lamp shells are fully as strange and unique as they are externally. Unlike true shells, they have a calcareous skeleton which is attached to the upper shell, as well as two coiled, tentacle-like extensions of the body. These are fringed with minute, hairlike cilia, which, by their vibrations, draw in a current of water containing the minute animals on which the lamp shells feed. In addition to thus supplying food, these tentacles serve as respiratory organs, or gills, and as nerves. Between the bases of the tentacles is the mouth opening, but there are no jaws or other accessories, the mouth being connected directly with the stomach and its sac-like intestine. In addition to the sensitive tentacles, there is a true nervous system consisting of two pairs of ganglia—which serve as a brain—with many nerves branching from them. There is also a heart with arteries and veins.

For opening and closing the shells there are two pairs of strong muscles. Finally, there is the anchor-stalk that may be extended or retracted at will; if the lamp shell decides to move to another spot it can hoist its anchor, swim about freely, and settle down in a new location. Taken all in all, brachiopods are very strange creatures, and it is not surprising that they were such a puzzle to the scientists, some of whom classed them among the mollusks, although others felt that the Brachiopoda belonged among the worms.

12

Lobsters and Their Cousins

Everyone knows the lobster, but few of those who relish the big crustacean's delectable flesh boiled, broiled, in lobster Newburg or served as a salad, know very little about the lobsters' lives or habits—or that a lobster is not always a lobster. If you should drop into a restaurant in Florida, the West Indies, Bermuda, South America or on our Pacific coast, and order lobster, it would be served minus claws; you might ask the reason why. The answer is that the so-called Florida, West Indian, or South American lobsters do not have claws. Actually they are not true lobsters but sea crayfish; if you insisted on being served real lobster in Florida you would be given Maine lobsters—at a very high price.

On the other hand, if you were dining in England or on the Continent you would find both lobster and crayfish on the menus, for both true lobsters with claws and the clawless "spiny lobster," or sea crayfish, inhabit the waters of Europe and the British Isles, although in this country the true lobsters will not survive in the warmer waters of the south.

If, having learned that the tropical "lobsters" are really maritime crayfish, you should order crayfish in the West

Indies or Mexico, you would be served still another kind of crustacean, lobsterlike creature with long, slender but strong claws, which inhabits the mountain streams and rivers and is fully as delicious as any lobster caught in the sea along our New England coast.

Whether or not the true lobster of the north or the "Florida" lobster of the south is the better—from a gastronomical standpoint—is debatable. A great deal depends upon the size of the creatures and the manner in which they are cooked. Northern lobsters over two or three pounds in weight are rarely served, whereas the sea crayfish or "Florida lobsters" may weigh ten or twelve pounds; even twenty or twenty-five pound individuals are common. Today, northern lobsters weighing ten pounds or more are very, very scarce and when a twenty-pounder is taken, it is front-page news. Yet when I was a boy these big fellows were quite common, and when the tide flowed out of the Bay of Fundy we could always gather dozens of big lobsters from under the exposed stones and ledges; many of these were monsters over twenty pounds in weight. Nobody ever considered eating these old-timers; they were fed to the hogs and only the small and medium-sized specimens were deemed suitable for the table.

Size for size, given the same method of cooking, there is not much difference between the flesh of the northern lobster and the sea crayfish in the matter of tenderness, but there is no question that the meat of the northern lobster is sweeter and better-flavored than that of the sea crayfish. Very often, however, the "lobsters" served in our northern restaurants are in reality sea crayfish. Of course the latter cannot be substituted for boiled or broiled lobster, but where the claws are not in evidence—as in lobster salad or lobster stew—it is difficult to identify the source of the meat.

At the present time the Florida lobsters are for sale in nearly all of our northern fish markets and are listed on the menus of many restaurants in New York and other large cities; the exportation of sea crayfish and crayfish tails from Florida and the Bahamas to the northern markets has become an enormous business and there is scarcely a portion of the country where crayfish are not obtainable.

The abundance of these sea crayfish is almost incredible. All through the season during which lobstering is legal in the Bahamas, scores of big ocean-going lobster boats ply steadily back and forth between the Bahamas and the Florida ports, making the round trip every week or ten days. On every trip their capacious holds are filled with thousands of crayfish packed in ice. As soon as they reach the fish docks, a certain proportion are repacked in barrels of ice to be shipped alive. Others are placed in huge vats and boiled; thousands of the tails are quick-frozen and shipped in cartons. It would seem as if the millions of these crustaceans caught in the Bahamas would soon deplete the supply, even though they are protected by a closed season, but apparently there has been no decrease in their numbers.

If you should watch these Florida lobsters being unloaded from the boats you would doubtless be surprised to see that they are red, for unlike our northern kind, which are greenish in life and only turn red when cooked, the sea crayfish are naturally reddish or orange and are handsomely decorated with eyelike spots. Hence their scientific name of *Palinurus argus*, or eyed spiny lobster.

Even without nipping claws these spiny lobsters may not be handled carelessly. The stout bases of their extremely long antennae are covered with thick, needle-sharp spines. Long, curved spines project from the front of the head; rows of spines stretch along the back of the shell;

and each segment of the tail is armed with razor-edged spines on both sides and in the center. Even when dead a spiny lobster is not an easy thing to handle without being "juked," as the West Indians say, and when the sea crayfish is alive and lively, swinging its armed antennae about and viciously jerking its tail, it can cut one's flesh badly if one does not know how to handle the creature.

Now, having straightened out the matter of when a lobster is not a lobster, let us return to the real lobsters of our northern seas, for we will find that, quite apart from their interest as food, they are strange creatures indeed.

It is odd that lobsters should be considered edible at all when we consider their habits. Few people will eat crows and no one would dream of dining on vultures, yet neither of these birds can compare with the lobster when it comes to the matter of feeding on carrion. Lobsters may at times prey upon other living creatures, but they are primarily scavengers and prefer carrion to fresh meat. However, our ideas of what is fit for food and what is not are largely a matter of habit or custom. Both swine and poultry devour carrion—and almost anything else—yet they are almost universally regarded as excellent food, which is as it should be, for the food upon which any creature subsists seldom effects the edibility of its flesh.

Although lobsters live in inaccessible locations and only a small percentage are taken in traps, they would have been practically exterminated long ago had it not been for the enactment of stringent laws limiting the legal size of lobsters to be marketed and the establishment of lobster hatcheries at various places along our coast. Lobsters are very prolific creatures. Every female will produce many thousand eggs each season; if one out of every five hundred baby lobsters survived and grew up, there would always be a good supply of lobsters for human consumption.

Young lobsters, however, lead a dangerous and precarious life from the time they hatch from the eggs until they acquire a hard protective shell and powerful claws. Every carnivorous sea creature is as fond of young lobsters as human beings are fond of the adults; fish, mollusks, crustaceans—practically all the meat-eating marine animals—destroy a very large portion of the immature lobsters. Undoubtedly Nature would have maintained the balance of maritime life, as far as lobsters were concerned, had not man come into the picture and completely upset the balance by the wholesale taking of lobsters.

In other words, the lobster fishermen destroyed the lobsters faster than they could breed and increase, for female as well as male lobsters were captured. The taking of every female during the breeding season meant the destruction of thousands of potential lobsters. Once the lobster population began to decline, the doom of the lobster was sealed. To make the matter worse, the demand for lobsters increased as the supply decreased. Within a comparatively short time our native lobsters would have become as extinct as the dodo, had not our Bureau of Fisheries taken a hand in the lobster problem. Female lobsters with eggs were protected in hatcheries and young lobsters were cared for there until they were large enough to look after themselves. Every year millions of the youngsters were given their freedom, but for some inexplicable reason there appeared to be no noticeable increase in the supply of grown lobsters.

Finally, by mere chance—as so often is the case with notable discoveries—someone discovered that young lobsters, hatched from the eggs in the tanks and artificially reared, did not dive to the bottom and hide among the rocks as did the wild youngsters. In their artificial environment they had lost the instinct to safeguard themselves;

when released they merely swam about near the surface, thus falling easy victims to all their natural enemies. If the lobster population was to be maintained or increased, some means had to be found to induce the young lobsters to seek hiding places safe from their foes.

The problem was finally solved by teaching the infant lobsters to dive by sliding them down a chute which led to the bottom of the tanks, repeating the process over and over. After a time the little creatures—who apparently possessed some intelligence or liked the fun—learned to dive of their own accord and as soon as released promptly dove to the bottom of the sea. Today every lobster hatchery has its professional lobster-diving teachers. The lobster population is increasing; there is little danger of the delectable crustaceans being fished out.

Although the "soft-shell" or "shedder" crabs are well known to all who enjoy sea food, comparatively few people know about soft-shell lobsters. Like all the crustaceans that are forced to throw off their armorlike shells when they are outgrown, lobsters change their outer garments whenever they become too tight for comfort. Very few people have ever watched a lobster in the act of shedding, for from that time until the new shell becomes hard they are helpless, and take care to safeguard themselves by retiring to some deep crevice in the rocks or to a den under a stone. But it is possible to observe a lobster as it sheds in an aquarium where there is no chance for it to hide.

When the time comes for the change, the lobster's shell splits open along the back; the two sides fold open; the head and forward part of the body, soft and flexible, come slowly forth; the antennae and legs, as well as the claws, are withdrawn from their hard coverings; the tail is freed and the soft, pulpy, naked-looking creature, motionless, waits for its skin to turn to shell. This does not take very long, and normally the transformed creature remains in hiding until the new shell is completely hardened. Not wanting to move about, the lobster cannot hunt for food. Sometimes the pangs of hunger will force one to seek food before its shell is thoroughly hard. Such individuals are frequently captured in the traps and are regarded as especially good eating.

Everyone who has seen these fellows must have noticed that one claw is almost always larger and heavier than the other. The answer to the puzzle is that the lobster's claws serve a dual purpose; each one is designed for a specific duty. With the smaller, more slender and pointed claw the lobster captures fish and other prey, drives off or attacks its enemies, and tears up its food. The larger, blunt-ended claw, with its broad, dull teeth, serves to chew shells and other hard creatures, to act as a shield when attacked, and to crush captured enemies to death.

Like all of the crustaceans, the lobster may lose one of its legs, an antennae, one or both claws, or various other portions of the anatomy, and will appear with all the missing parts replaced with its next change of skin. Often, however, some minor injury to a leg or claw may result in the formation of a freak appendage; it is not unusual to come across a lobster with one claw doubled or with two legs where there should be one. These abnormalities are not always the results of injuries; often they occur at birth —just as some persons are born with six or more fingers or toes.

Although the lobster is rather sedentary in its habits and does not wander very far from its chosen lair, it is an excellent swimmer. By rapidly extending its tail and spasmodically flapping it forward, the lobster propels itself backward, its legs, claws, and antennae trailing in its wake.

Another interesting fact about lobsters is that they may

be hypnotized quickly and easily. I have known many an old lobsterman who had never heard of hypnotizing a lobster and stared incredulously when he saw a number of his lobsters standing on their heads and folded claws with tails in air, perfectly motionless. Anyone can hypnotize a lobster. Place it with its nose resting on a flat surface with the claws partially supporting it, bend the tail inward, and at the same time stroke the back from tail to head. When you remove your hands it will remain in this ridiculous position for an indefinite time. To be sure, this is not really hypnosis but is due to some temporary paralysis of the nervous system induced by the unnatural posture and the stroking of the creature's back. It is very similar to "hypnotizing" a hen by placing its head under its wing and whirling it about a few times—an old trick well known to all farmers.

Since northern lobsters rely so much upon their claws for fighting and for capturing and cutting up their food, you may wonder how the clawless sea crayfish manage to survive. Unlike northern lobsters, who devour dead fish, live fish, shells, other crustaceans and almost anything else, the crayfish devour only small creatures that do not have to be torn to bits in order to be swallowed, as well as carrion that is so thoroughly decomposed that it almost falls to pieces. The legs with the brush-covered tips serve very well for seizing the small fry as the crayfish lie in wait in their dens, their long whiplike antennae extended to catch the least vibration of the water caused by some moving object.

Quite frequently, if you watch these spiny lobsters carefully, you will see them rub the bases of the antennae across the forehead, producing a faint, rasping sound somewhat like that made on a violin string by rubbing a matchstick across it. As far as I know these creatures are the only crustaceans capable of producing an audible sound. Obviously the crayfish can converse or at least communicate by means of these notes, for if there are other crayfish near at hand they will wave their antennae, rise high on their feet, swing their heads toward the sounds and show every indication of listening. Moreover, careful tests have proved that the spiny lobsters can and do produce a variety of sounds which are supposedly "picked up" or heard by the sensatory hairs on their legs. As one scientist put it, they talk through their noses and hear with their feet.

The crayfish, like our northern lobster, is an expert swimmer; when swimming or walking on the sea bottom it moves far more rapidly than the true lobsters. Its speed is partly due to its much longer legs and more powerful tail and partly because it is not hampered by heavy, cumbersome claws. Like the ordinary lobster and other crustaceans, the sea crayfish shed their shelly skins and produce new legs or other appendages to replace those that have been lost or injured. They are far more hardy than any other crustacean I have ever seen; they will survive the loss of a large portion of their bodies, even though it cannot be replaced.

In many localities where these creatures are captured or where they are kept in corrals or enclosures to be sold, it is customary for the vendors to break off the tails and throw away the carapace, with its legs and antennae. One might reasonably expect that this severance of the tail and body would kill the creatures; on the contrary, as soon as the discarded portions are thrown overboard and sink to the bottom of the water, the mutilated creatures walk about, wave their antennae and show no indication of being in the least inconvenienced by the loss of the greater part of their anatomy. They will even eat, despite the fact that they lack an intestine.

I do not know how long they will continue to live in this condition; it would be an interesting experiment to place them in an aquarium where they would be safe, and thus learn just how long a half-crayfish will live. But they do not have a chance to survive for more than half an hour or so when cast overboard at the fish docks, for the water swarms with scavenger fish, mainly the big green parrot fish or "pugs," who quickly make a meal of the courageous but mutilated crayfish.

In the same waters where the spiny lobsters are found there is an even stranger crustacean known as the flat lobster and, in the Lesser Antilles, as sea cockroach or *ravitte del mar*, the latter names referring to its form and not its habits. If clean living means clean flesh, then the flat lobster should be the most preferable of all edible crustaceans, for it feeds entirely upon small living creatures and abhors carrion. As a matter of fact, the flat lobster is the best-tasting of all, far better flavored than even the best Maine lobsters. Yet in the Bermudas and in some of the West Indies it is not thought fit for human consumption. On the other hand, some gourmets regard this creature's flesh as far superior to that of the spiny lobster—and I heartily agree with them.

In appearance the flat lobster is unlike the true lobster or the sea crayfish. Actually, it is not closely related to either, and in many ways is more like a gigantic cockroach than like a lobster—despite the fact that it is a decapod (in other words, it has ten legs) like the true lobsters, crayfish, shrimp, and crabs, all of which are edible and economically important. The similarity between a flat lobster and a cockroach is all on the outside and is due mainly to the flat lobster's rough, dull-colored carapace and tail and its short, weak legs, which are usually tucked out of sight beneath the body. Moreover, instead of claws and

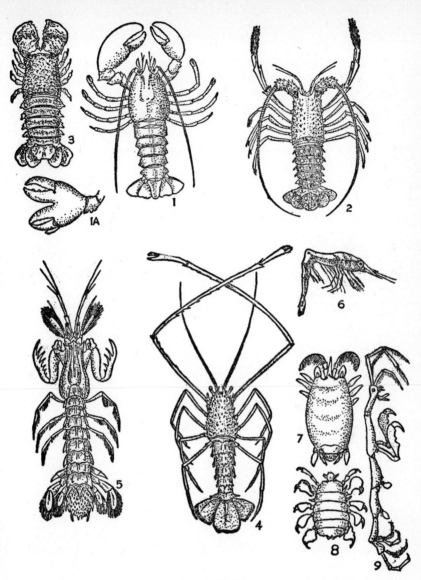

PLATE V

1. *Common lobster*   1a. *Freak claw of lobster*   2. *Spiny lobster, or sea crayfish*   3. *Flat lobster, or sea cockroach*   4. *The Archer* 5. *Mantis shrimp, or squilla*   6. *Red-white-and-blue shrimp (patriotic shrimp)*   7. *Hippa, or sand bug*   8. *Whale louse*   9. *The weird Caprella shrimp*

long antennae, the flat lobster has a pair of flat, wide plates with rounded edges on the outer rims and sawlike teeth on the inner edges; these are kept folded in front of the head when not in use.

Unlike either the lobster or the crayfish, which dwell in holes in rock, the flat lobster inhabits the bottom of the sea among the corals and stones, where it moves about, half-buried in the sand or mud, using its flattened front claws as shovels. Here, among the coral growths, sponges, and weeds, the flat lobster's rough, brownish or grayish body, mottled with rusty red or orange, is so perfectly camouflaged that it is almost invisible when not in motion. Lacking any means of self-defense when it is frightened, the flat lobster folds its short legs beneath the body, rolls up like an armadillo, covers the soft underparts with the broad front legs, and is transformed into a rough ball far too hard to be harmed by any ordinary foe.

There are several species of these flat lobsters, but all are much alike except in color and size. Unfortunately for people who are aware of the delicious flesh within the creature's armor plate, they never grow very large, rarely weighing more than two or three pounds. But pound for pound they are far more meaty than either lobsters or crayfish; the flesh is so rich that a two-pound flat lobster will make a hearty meal for the average person.

Another edible crustacean that inhabits the West Indian seas and is quite often captured in traps set for spiny lobsters is a queer creature resembling an attenuated lobster. It has enormously long claws equipped with small but powerful nippers, long antennae and legs, and a large, broad tail. This vivid red or orange crustacean is known to scientists as *Sagittarius*, the Archer; the curved front legs are kept crossed, the antennae lying over them, giving the effect of a bent bow.

They are not large creatures, seldom weighing more than two or three pounds. Most of the weight is in the legs, so that the Archer contains comparatively little flesh. Its fine quality compensates for the quantity; I do not think there is any crustacean, large or small, whose meat can compare with that of the Archer.

Still another member of the edible decapod crustaceans that inhabits the northern as well as the southern seas is the squilla, or mantis shrimp. If anything, it is even more strange in appearance than the flat lobster. Long and slender, with a tucked-in waistline, a broad tail, and a small, hard thorax, the squilla is handsomely colored in brown, green, yellow, and rose. Thus it is a conspicuous object when swimming swiftly through the water, although most of the time it keeps out of sight in deep burrows or under stones. At first these creatures appear to have only eight legs including the "claws," but if we examine one closely we will find that the missing pair of legs has been modified to form paddle-shaped swimming organs on either side of the hard, spiny tail-plate. But the most striking feature of the squilla is its "claws," or front legs. Instead of being equipped with true claws or nippers, those of the squilla have long, needle-sharp spines along the inner edge of the terminal section; these fit into grooves on the next section. Moreover, the creature's claws move vertically rather than laterally; it invariably holds them in a prayerful position, in exactly the same manner as the insect known as the praying mantis.

If they have the chance, they will decide that discretion is the better part of valor, and dodge quickly into their holes when danger threatens. But if cornered, they will put up a terrific, savage fight. Few sea creatures of their size are better equipped by Nature for fighting. They can slash wickedly with their spine-clad tails and tooth-edged tail-plate, and their claws are deadly weapons.

Never underestimate the fighting ability of one of these little creatures—and never hold one unless you know how, for the needle-sharp claw spines will pierce one's finger or thumb (as I know from painful experience), and once the jaws close they are so firmly locked that it is impossible to open them without breaking them from the creature, or until the squilla is relaxed in death.

13

Shrimp and Prawns

AMONG the most valuable and important food products of the sea are shrimp and prawns. There are hundreds of species of edible shrimp, but only a few are large enough or occur in sufficient numbers to be of any economic importance. Few people—even lovers of shrimp cocktails, salads, and curries—realize what vast quantities of shrimp are taken from the sea. Shrimp fishers work in Asian, European, African, Australian, West Indian, and North and South American waters. In California alone the yearly catch is valued at over $150,000. Vast numbers of the crustaceans are taken along our North Atlantic coast. Tons upon tons are caught off Florida's east coast and in the Gulf of Mexico.

Not too long ago, the principal shrimp fisheries in the United States centered about Fernandina, Florida, and Biloxi, Mississippi. Prolific as shrimp are, the netting of vast quantities gradually decreased the population. Fewer and fewer were taken; shrimp boat after shrimp boat went out of business. Then, quite by accident, a shrimper dropped nets at night off Key West, Florida. During the day, so few shrimp had been taken that the catch did not pay expenses. To the utter amazement of the shrimper, the nets put down at night came up bursting with shrimp —not the ordinary daytime shrimp, but huge, luscious, rosy-pink shrimp unlike any the shrimper had ever seen. Again and again the dredge-nets were dragged over the bottom; at every haul they came up filled to overflowing.

The news spread like wildfire. Boats that had been decommissioned were hastily remanned and put to sea. Soon hundreds of shrimp boats dotted the waters of the Gulf. From near and far they came: from the Carolinas, from Virginia—even from New England; from Louisiana, Mississippi, Alabama, and Texas. An incredibly big shrimp harvest was reaped by all, as the nets and dredges were dropped and dragged at night. Frequently a shrimp boat would take hundreds of dollars worth of shrimp between darkness and dawn, even though during the day none could be caught. Never in the history of the shrimp fisheries had there been such a catch.

The crustaceans were brought to Key West, Fort Meyers, and other Florida ports in such vast numbers that the docks and packing houses were filled. Men toiled rapidly to increase the size and capacity of sheds, wharves, freezers, and canning machinery. Hundreds of new employees were hired; trainloads and truckloads of canned, iced, and boiled shrimp sped north, east, and west, carrying the giant pink shrimp to every part of the country.

Soon after the night shrimping began, another discovery was made. This one was important to the conchologists, who had no interest whatsoever in shrimp. Almost every dredge or trawl drawn up by the shrimpers contained sea shells. To the amazement and joy of the collectors, many of the shells were species that had hitherto been extremely rare. The conchologists hurried to the shrimping ports;

soon the shrimpers were doing a thriving business in sea shells, for which they would frequently receive more than for their shrimp.

All good things come to an end, however. Fewer and fewer shrimp were taken; first one by one and then in groups and flotillas the shrimp boats headed for their home ports, but their captains and crews had become richer than they had ever hoped in their wildest dreams.

Meanwhile our government had become interested in the strange new shrimp and their nighttime abundance; scientists from the Bureau of Fisheries cruised the Gulf of Mexico, searching for shrimp, striving to learn what had become of them and whether any great number still survived. Finally the mystery was solved: the shrimp had migrated. They had deserted the seas about Key West and the Dry Tortugas and were swarming in great numbers off the coast of Mexico and Yucatán. A huge fleet of shrimp boats steamed back and forth over the Bank of Campeche. In addition to those flying the Stars and Stripes, there were scores flying the red, white, and green flag of Mexico; soon little ports like Carmen, Campeche, and Progreso were becoming shrimp boom-towns, enjoying the greatest prosperity they had known since the good old days of buccaneers and pirates.

Naturally, international complications arose. The Mexicans were as averse to allowing the American shrimpers in Mexican waters as our government would be to foreign fishing craft in American waters. Several American boats were seized and their crews were arrested. Diplomatic notes passed back and forth; for a time there were threats of open violence and bloodshed. At last, however, all differences were amicably adjusted and today the Mexican and the North American shrimpers gather their rich harvests side by side—except that our vessels do not fish within the legal limits of Mexican waters.

For a year and more the great fleet of over 500 boats steadily took tons of shrimp from the western Gulf. But once again a decrease in the number of shrimp was noted, and the shrimpers, following the movement of the vast shrimp swarms, sailed southward. Where or when this migration will end no one knows, for the ways of shrimp are beyond human understanding, despite the long and intensive study that scientists have devoted to them.

At one time it was thought that shrimp wandered about but little, and that the shrimp off east Florida, those in the Gulf, and the ones in New England waters were all separate colonies. But by "banding" the shrimp, the scientists learned that the little crustaceans travel all the way from Florida and the Gulf of Mexico to Maine and back each year! Considering the size of shrimp and the fact that they are the favorite food of innumerable fish, squids, octopuses, crabs, lobsters, and other sea creatures, it is remarkable that any survived their long round trip to New England waters. Yet they not only survived but increased to such numbers that for many, many years they have been caught by millions and have brought large fortunes to the shrimp industry.

Quite apart from their economic and food value, shrimp, or prawns, are interesting creatures. Whether we call them shrimp or prawns depends largely on their size. Quite often large individuals of a species will be called prawns, whereas small specimens of the same species will be classed as shrimp, especially in England.

The majority of the shrimp consumed in this country are in the prawn class, but the British, the French, and especially the Chinese, are fully as fond of the small "shrimp." In France, tiny shrimp an inch or less in length are served

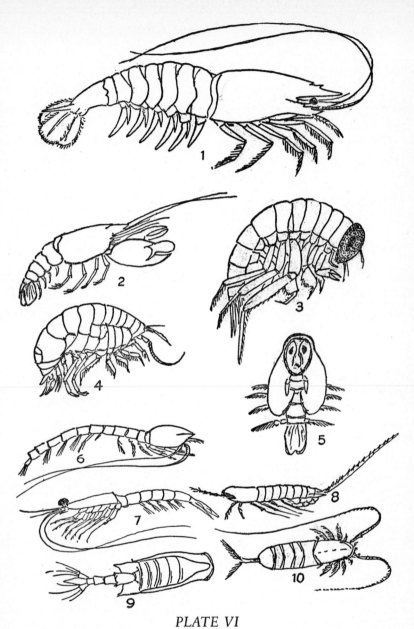

PLATE VI

1. *Common shrimp, or prawn*   2. *Snapping shrimp (Alpheus)*
3, 4. *Sand hoppers, or sand fleas*   5. *Copepod*   6-10. *Brit shrimp*

in nearly all restaurants. Tiny shrimp are considered a great delicacy in England. In far-off China, as well as in Mexico, vast quantities of these small shrimp are caught and dried; when they are soaked in water and properly cooked, they are very tasty and fully as good as any kind of fresh shrimp.

Scientifically speaking, the true shrimp are close relatives of the lobsters, for they are ten-footed creatures—or decapods. Their structure is similar to the lobster, and although many are clawless, some have claws far larger and more powerful in proportion to their size than those of any lobster.

Like the lobsters, the shrimp have long slender antennae, a jointed abdomen, and a broad tail made up of several movable plates which may be spread wide or closely folded. Between the stalked eyes there is a long, sharp, notched extension of the shell, with saw-edged points between the eyes and the first leglike appendages. The latter are known as maxillipeds and are used to push food into the shrimp's jaws. Back of the maxillipeds, or "jaw feet," are the five pairs of true feet. Some of these end in hooks, some in small lobsterlike claws; others have sharp-tipped ends.

On either side of the abdomen are five jointed, flexible appendages edged with stiff hair and known as "swimmerets." They serve as oars when the shrimp swims, rapidly darting here and there; unlike lobsters, shrimp are very active little creatures and never remain long at rest on the bottom of the sea.

There are a great many species of shrimp and they vary as much in form, habits, and other respects as in size. Many species are so transparent that only their internal organs are visible in clear water; some have such broad, flat bodies and such short legs that they look more like crabs than shrimp; others have enormously long legs which are out of all proportion to their bodies. Most of the species that are not transparent are dull-colored in browns, grays, or greens; others are brilliantly colored.

One very striking long-legged species, quite common under rocks and in crevices in Florida and the West Indies, is a most patriotic-looking chap; he is decorated with red, white, and blue stripes. Another species is flaming red. Nearly all are phosphorescent; one species ejects a cloud of luminous material to conceal its whereabouts when threatened by an enemy.

14

Snappers, Hoppers, and Hippas

SEARCHING for shells or sea creatures along our southern coast or in the West Indies, you might be mystified by sharp cracking or snapping sound apparently issuing from solid rocks or coral. Certainly none of the visible creatures are the source of the sounds, which have an odd metallic click and are as loud as the noise made by snapping one's fingers. No sea anemone, sponge, coral, or gorgonian is snapping its fingers at you; yet no other living creatures are visible.

If your curiosity demands a solution to the mystery, lift some of the rocks or break away a piece of the coral; as the chorus of sharp cracking sounds increases in volume, you will uncover many small shrimp looking like miniature lobsters. Each has one huge claw that seems far too large for the shrimp's body.

These are the strange decapod crustaceans known as snapping shrimp. They are lively little chaps who dwell in holes and crannies, keeping well out of sight. Their bodies are similar to that of the common shrimp: they have long slender antennae, a segmented abdomen with swimmerets, and four pairs of true legs in addition to the claws. One of the claws is equipped with slender nippers; the other is enormous and seemingly deformed. This huge claw is the shrimp's snapper; the astonishingly loud noise is produced by partially dislocating the wrist joint and then snapping it back into place, exactly as some people can make a cracking sound by dislocating a finger or toe joint at will.

How, you may wonder, can a tiny shrimp make such a racket by snapping its minute wrist joint? The answer is that the big claw acts as a sound box, amplifying the noise exactly as the hollow body of a violin or a guitar amplifies the music produced by the strings. There are many species of these snapping shrimp; some prefer holes and crevices in rocks, others the cavities in dead coral. A number dwell in sponges, and several have their homes in piles of dead oyster shells or in oyster beds. Nearly all are conspicuously colored, some being gaudy creatures with brilliant red, orange, or purple claws and back, or with the big sound-making claws parti-colored. Just why these odd crustaceans should betray their presence when disturbed, instead of remaining silently in their hiding places, is something of a mystery.

The most logical explanation is that the snapping noises are made to drive away their foes, such as fish and other predatory marine animals. Of course, they do not realize that man is not terrified by the chorus of snapping sounds. To a fish or other natural enemy the snappings may sound like deafening explosions with intense vibrations. To the shrimp's ordinary foes they look as large as lobsters would to us; imagine what a racket hundreds of the creatures would make were they the size of big lobsters!

Hidden away in the corals and rocks are many strange crustaceans. Some, when uncovered or disturbed, scurry along searching for new hiding places, or roll up into little balls like the familiar pill bugs so common under stones on land. Others leap into the air as if activated by coiled springs, while still others, whose courage is far out of proportion to their size, back into some crevice and wave their tiny claws menacingly. If you are lucky you may discover some of the strange "possum" shrimp, so called because they carry their eggs in a pouch much as their namesakes carry their young.

One of the best places to find strange crustaceans is among the windrows of seaweed cast up on the beach. Here are swarms of the crustaceans. Most of them are hopping; as the dead seaweed is disturbed hundreds of little shrimplike creatures leap and spring in every direction. Although they all are crustaceans, only a few are true shrimp, the majority of the creatures being copepods, isopods, amphipods, and other "pods" (to the scientist, but usually called "sand fleas" by most of us).

Over ten thousand species of the small crustaceans are known; doubtless fully as many have never been described by scientists. The jumpers and hoppers are usually amphipods; the isopods and copepods are crawling and swimming crustaceans. Many species neither crawl, swim, nor hop; they are parasites. Several species are fish parasites; others live off fellow crustaceans. Crabs, lobsters, shrimp, and hermit crabs all suffer from these vampirish creatures.

Most destructive, perhaps, is the *Sacculina*, which plays havoc with crabs, destroying thousands annually. The *Sacculina* is a crustacean, although it looks like nothing but a sac-like object at the tip of a stalk. Once it obtains a foothold on a crab the latter is doomed to a slow and lingering death; with great rapidity the roots of the parasite divide and subdivide, finding their way through the shell and into the living tissue of the victim, even penetrating to the extremities of the legs and claws. Eventually the parasite devours the crab alive. It might be supposed that when the crab sheds its shell it would also rid itself of the parasite, but once a crab is attacked by the *Sacculina* it never again sheds its shell.

Even whales have their crustacean parasites, which are more like lice than crustaceans. And like true lice and spiders, the whale lice, as they are called, have eight legs, each of which terminates in a strong, hooked claw that enables the parasites to cling fast to the slippery skin of the whale. Although they do not injure the huge cetaceans, they are as irritating as real lice, and cause the whales to itch intolerably, especially when they congregate by hundreds on the great creature's lips and eyelids, or in back of the flippers. Incapable of scratching themselves with their own tails or flippers, the whales rub themselves against masses of driftwood, coral growths, or any other rough surface. Many whales become stranded on the beaches because, in their desire to alleviate the itching caused by the parasites, they rub themselves against reefs and rocks too close to shore for safety.

Quite different from these repulsive parasites are the majority of the crustaceans we find among the seaweed and other debris on our beaches. Despite the popular idea that these so-called sand fleas can bite, they are perfectly harmless. The biting is done by tiny flies or gnats which breed in beach trash. Moreover, true fleas are prevalent on beaches, especially where there have been many dogs, but the innocent little crustaceans get the blame for the irritating bites.

The hoppers and rollers teeming in dead algae are scavengers and thus very useful creatures, since they play a large part in keeping our beaches clean. We might laugh at the idea of such tiny creatures having any visible effect on the cleanliness or lack of it on a long, wide beach, but we must remember that there are droves of them in their

sanitary squads. One man might have a hard job cleaning up a five- or ten-mile beach every day, but ten thousand men all working at the job would make short work of
it. On most beaches five or so miles in length, millions of
the scavenger crustaceans come forth from their hiding
places during the night. Dead fish, dead birds, even large
masses of carrion, quickly disappear as multitudes of the
hungry crustaceans swarm over the decaying flesh. Every
vestige of food and paper left on the beach by human beings vanishes as if by magic, for many of these crustaceans are vegetarians as well as meat-eaters.

Anything of vegetable origin is welcome to them; in a
very short time they will completely destroy large pieces of
driftwood and even logs and tree trunks. Some species
honeycomb the wood with funnels, feeding as they bore,
until the timber or board disintegrates completely. Others
gnaw shallow holes in wood; as the weakened layer breaks
off the creatures repeat the process, thus dining on a layer
of wood at a time—until nothing remains.

These scavenging crustaceans are not only most helpful
in keeping the beaches clean; they also aid scientists and
act as laboratory assistants by preparing the skeletons of
animals. When a scientist, or rather an osteologist, wishes
to enlist the services of the crustaceans, he places the car-
cass to be skeletonized in a screen-covered receptacle or a
net bag and anchors it between low- and high-water marks.
As the tide rises and covers the dead animal, thousands of
tiny crustaceans rush to the feast; by the time the tide has
receded only the cleanly stripped bones remain, forming a
skeleton as clean, white and perfect as the most exacting
scientist could wish. Best of all, the tough cartilage that
holds the bones together remains uninjured, leaving the
skeletons fully articulated and saving the hours of patient,
skilled labor needed to assemble and connect the bones. It

is a tedious and difficult job to connect all the bones of a
snake or a fish in their proper places; but in this case every
bone will be joined and in its place when the tide ebbs,
carrying away the army of creatures who have done the
job for the scientist.

These busy scavengers seem possessed by a mania for
cleanliness. Not satisfied with patrolling the beaches and
keeping them sanitary, they turn their attentions to creatures inhabiting the adjacent waters, and take on the
duties of janitors for such animals as sea stars and sea urchins. Crawling about among the spines of the echinoderms, they industriously pick off and destroy all bits of
rubbish and dirt that lodges on their hosts. Several thousand of these house cleaners may be found on a single sea
star or other echinoderm, and more than twenty thousand
have been taken from one sea urchin. To be sure, theirs
is not a wholly unselfish job, for much of the debris they
remove is food to them; thus they get free board and lodg-
ing for their labors.

Another strange and interesting crustacean is the caprella, which you will find clinging to seaweed or to a hydroid or bryozoan. If the creature is motionless, it might
readily be mistaken for a portion of the object on which it
rests. If the caprella is crawling about, it resembles a
"measuring worm," moving forward by alternately grasping
an object with its front feet, arching its body, advancing
its rear feet and grasping the object on which it is crawling; then it straightens out and stretches forward as far as
it can reach, grips hold with its front feet and repeats the
entire operation over and over again. From its appearance
no one ever would guess the creature is a crustacean and
not a caterpillar. Its long, slender body is composed of segments; there are no indications of a thorax or an abdomen.
The antennae are short, as are the rear legs. Instead of a

fanlike tail there is a hooked grasping appendage; the two front legs are equipped with strong hooked claws somewhat like those of the mantis shrimp.

No chapter on crustaceans would be complete without mention of the hippas, those active little creatures that swarm by thousands on beaches below the high water mark, but whose presence is unknown and unsuspected by most people. Hippas are strange-looking creatures with olive-shaped bodies, short, strong legs and long, feathery, curled antennae.

In their habits and appearance they somewhat resemble moles; they are quite commonly known as "mole shrimp." They are not true shrimp, but are in a family by themselves and are scientifically classed as crabs. At first sight the hippa seems to consist entirely of a smooth, brownish thorax or carapace, but if we turn one of the creatures over on its back we will find that it has a jointed abdomen ending in a pointed, rigid tail that is kept folded tightly against the creature's underside.

In the areas where the hippas abound you will come upon another and somewhat similar crustacean known as albunea by scientists. Although the two have almost identical habits, dwell side by side, and are commonly called sand bugs or sand hoppers, there is little resemblance between them. Unlike the hippa, with its rounded, oval back, the albunea is almost rectangular in outline and the shell is marked by creases and lines that give it the effect of being composed of several plates. Along the front edge there are short spines, with a larger spine at each corner. Instead of the handsome plumelike antennae of the hippa, this chap has long jointed antennae like those of the lobster; and its short, stout legs end in strong, flat hooks like shovels. Also, the abdomen is much shorter than in the hippas and ends in a flat plate instead of a spine. But like its hippa comrades, it carries its tail folded up and tightly pressed against its abdomen. Both of these odd creatures seek safety by burying themselves in the sand, but if by chance they are left exposed when danger threatens they tuck in their heads, tails, and legs, and transpose themselves into semi-spherical objects that might well be mistaken for pebbles.

Buried in the sand at the edge of the waves, the albuneas always maintain their position as the tides ebb and flow. As the tide rises and covers their burrows, they pop out of the sand and scurry beneath the water to the limit of the wave, where they vanish as if by magic. When the tide turns and begins to ebb, they reverse the process, emerging from their burrows, rushing down the beach, and disappearing in the sand at the water's edge. In many places bordering the sea there is a difference of twenty feet between the tides; the little crustaceans must travel back and forth for what must seem to them many miles, every twenty-four hours.

Even if most persons never suspect the presence of these busy creatures, both their presence and their habits are well known to birds and to fishermen. Hippas are excellent bait for certain fish, and in places where they abound one may see dozens of men and boys standing in the water with specially designed nets which they drag along the sandy bottom. Each time a wave comes in, they capture hundreds of creatures who are leaving their burrows to follow the waves before digging in once more.

The hippas are edible and far more delicate than any shrimp, but in the north they are never regarded as food. In South America, especially in Peru, they are important sea food. On the Pacific coast, which has a tremendous rise and fall of tides, the hippas are more numerous than along our shores. And the vast areas of sand exposed between high and low water marks favor the hippa hunters, who aph5 tags.

frequently gather bushels of the creatures between the ebb and flow of a tide.

The worst enemies of the hippas are not human beings but the shore and sea birds. Wherever these crustaceans abound they attract flocks of shore birds of all sizes, from little sandpipers to big curlews, all running nimbly back and forth at the edges of the waves, darting their bills into the water to seize the hippas as they momentarily appear. Overhead, terns, gulls, skimmers, and other sea birds wing back and forth, constantly swooping down to capture the little crustaceans when they rush from their burrows to their next hideouts.

In no other part of the world, I believe, have the hippa-hunting birds developed such a perfect system and technique as on the coast of Peru. Here, thousands of the gray noddy terns devote all of their waking hours to feeding on the hippas. It is fascinating to watch them; they are so preoccupied with their hippa-catching that they pay little or no attention to human beings standing a few feet away. As each receding breaker leaves the sand bare, the entire flock of birds half runs, half flutters forward to seize the hippas before they vanish into their burrows. Then, as the next wave comes roaring in, the noddys take wing and settle down on shore well beyond reach of the surf. There they stand, alert and poised, to rush forward the instant the white-frothed water begins to recede.

15

Barnacles and Brant

EVERY seashore visitor is familiar with barnacles; the pesky things cover rocks, driftwood and other objects, and are a menace to swimmers. Boatmen and sailors heartily dislike barnacles, which attach themselves to the bottoms of boats, greatly reducing their speed, besides affording a root-hold for seaweed, sea grass, and all sorts of marine growths. I do not believe that they have a single friend in the world; although they have an abundance of enemies among the sea creatures, they are so well protected that they suffer little from the claws, jaws, or suckers of their foes.

Although we think of barnacles as nuisances and pay little or no attention to them, aside from giving them a wide berth when in bathing, they are perhaps the most remarkable of all the crustaceans. "Crustaceans!" you may exclaim, "surely those hard-shelled, sharp-edged things so firmly fastened to solid objects cannot be crustaceans." Nevertheless they are, despite the fact that many people consider them some sort of a sea shell or mollusk.

We are accustomed to thinking of barnacles as immovably fixed objects enclosed in hard shells, but like many other sea creatures that are firmly anchored, their

131

young swim about freely. The mobile life of the nauplius, the larval barnacle, does not last long, however. Soon it settles down, attaches itself to a rock, and changes both its skin and its habits. The new skin is protected by six or more triangular sections of hard, calcareous material with interlocking edges, hinged bases and a trap-door cover of the same material. The several sections, as well as the lid of the wigwam-like structure, are attached to the skin of

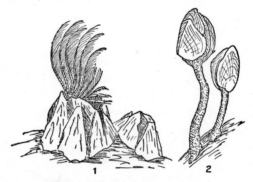

1. *Barnacles expanded and closed*
2. *Goose barnacles*

the creature and to various muscles, so that they may be moved at will. Having shed its old skin and acquired an almost impregnable limestone house, the barnacle pushes up its trap door and swings the side walls outward. Then, through the skylight, as one might say, it lifts its plume-like, jointed legs and moves them back and forth, seeking its food.

Since it was fasting while being transformed from a free-swimming nauplius to a barnacle, it is naturally hungry, but now that it is permanently anchored and cannot move about to obtain food, it is forced to bring the food to it. However, Nature has provided the creature with the means to solve the problem. The legs, with their fringes of hundreds of fine hairs, vibrate, producing a current in the water and drawing innumerable tiny organisms within the barnacle's reach and thence into the mouth. As one famous scientist remarked, "The barnacle is a crustacean that stands on its head and kicks food into its mouth with its legs."

Although the creature's head and eyes are at the bottom of its house, it is extremely sensitive to any unusual movement or vibration in the water, as well as to light and shade. If a shadow falls across its home, if some object approaches through the water, or if the barnacle feels an unusual vibration, it instantly withdraws its legs, pulls the trap door shut and draws the encircling plates together and locks them. Then it is perfectly safe within its little fortress.

In many places barnacles grow well above low-water mark, but when the tide recedes and leaves them exposed to air and sunshine they do not suffer for want of water. Closing their doors as the tide ebbs and their senses warn that they will soon be left high and dry, the barnacles shut the skylights and walls, enclosing enough water to serve their needs until the tide rises and covers them once more. If you listen carefully in a spot where thousands of barnacles cover rocks or piles, you will hear constant hissing and rattling sounds as the tide falls and myriads of barnacles shut up their houses for five or six hours. Many a swimmer has been mystified at hearing strange clapping noises as he swam by old piers or submerged rocks, never suspecting the sounds were made by barnacles alarmed at his presence and hurriedly shutting up shop.

Although there is a general similarity between all of the fixed barnacles, there are a great many species, each quite different from the others in the form and "sculpture" of its plates and in other details. Some are quite slender and tall; others are broad and flat. Many never become large, whereas others grow to immense size. Some species never occur above the low-water mark, but others are most abundant between the limits of high and low water—and still others live in deep water.

The majority of barnacles will attach themselves to almost any object, either stationary or floating, but some species are very particular and will only settle down to a sedentary life on certain kinds of shells, crabs, or other crustaceans, or on certain kinds of seaweed or other marine growths. A number prefer to lead the life of hitchhikers, and fasten themselves to sea turtles, sharks and even whales.

Aside from these run-of-the-mill barnacles, so familiar to all who visit the seashore, there are strange kinds that grow on the ends of long, fleshy, flexible stems. You may have noticed these odd creatures on the beach, attached to bits of driftwood or other flotsam cast up by the waves, but you probably never suspected they were barnacles, for they bear very little resemblance to those with which we are familiar. These "goose barnacles," as they are called, are usually attached to the underside of floating driftwood, to the lower shells of sea turtles or to the bottoms of vessels, where they are almost constantly moving through the water, but some species attach their stalks to the piles of wharfs, rocks and other stationary objects.

Although, as I have said, these creatures do not resemble the ordinary barnacles, if we examine them carefully we will find that the clamlike shell at the free end of the tough stalk is very similar in its details to the conical houses of the common barnacles. This oval-shaped barnacle is made up of five plates so placed that the whole resembles a bivalve sea shell. But if we should watch a live goose barnacle in water we would see the familiar plumed legs extended from the shell, kicking food into the strange creature's mouth in exactly the same manner as the common barnacles.

Perhaps you wonder why these creatures are called goose barnacles. The name goes back to the days when intelligent men were just beginning to take an interest in the living creatures about them, and the so-called naturalists were credulous and woefully ignorant of the truth about the many strange creatures of both land and sea. All were familiar with the odd creatures which were attached to various objects in the water and had crooked, fleshy stalks terminating in a white egg-shaped shell. They also knew that the brant geese gathered in flocks where these barnacles usually abounded.

So someone jumped to the conclusion that the long-necked barnacles were the brants' eggs, and to prove his assumption he published pictures of the barnacles with young geese issuing from them and swimming about in the water. In his "Generale Historie of Plants," published in 1597, the naturalist-botanist John Gerard wrote: "There are founde in the North parts of Scotland and the islandes called Orchades, certaine trees whereon do growe certaine shell fishes of a white colour, tending to russet, wherein are contained little living creatures; which shells in time of maturitie do open, and out of them growe those living foules whom we call barnacles, in the North of England brant geise, and in Lancashire tree geise. But those that do fall upon land do perish and come to nothing." To prove the truth of this remarkable tale, the author added: "What our eies have seen and our hands have touched, we shall so declare."

For centuries it has been known that the tale was pure imaginative fiction, but we still refer to the strange crustaceans as goose barnacles—and the brant are called "barnacle geese."

16

Strangest of Crustaceans

Although we often speak of "clear" or "pure" water, no natural water—whether fresh or salt—is either clear or pure. To be sure, a jar of ocean water collected far from land will look as clear as crystal, but if we place a small quantity of this seemingly pure water under a microscope, we will find that it swarms with organisms. There will be minute vegetable growths—such as diatoms—and tiny animals swimming about in every possible direction.

Some we may recognize as Foraminifera, already described in Chapter 1; others may be tiny jellyfish. There will be threadlike swimming worms, as well as creatures unlike anything we have ever before seen, some of which are so transparent that their presence is only revealed by their darker, more opaque internal organs.

As we watch the teeming life contained in our sample of "clear" sea water, we will appreciate the truth of the saying "The sea is full of wonderful things." And among the most wonderful are certain strange crustaceans. Moreover, there are many species, all different, and some with such weird, grotesque shapes that they appear more like monstrosities than normal forms of life. Some look like miniature horsefoot crabs; others resemble shrimp with extremely long, slender tails; still others, with rounded bodies and trailing hairs, dash about with jerking motions.

Among the strangest of all are the swiftly-swimming creatures with forked tails and a single black eye in the center of their blunt heads, known to scientists as the Cyclops. Known to fishermen as "brit," they are of great value to man; our most important fishing industry is dependent upon the brit, the principal food for herring. Great fleets of vessels bring the herring into port. Armies of men and women are needed to clean, salt, dry, and smoke the fish; throughout the world thousands of tons of herring are consumed in one form or another, including the cheaper grades of the so-called sardines, which are really small herring under a pseudonym.

Many a port on our own coast owes its existence to herring; far more of the seacoast towns of England, Scotland, Norway, Sweden, Denmark, Holland, France, and elsewhere would become ghost towns should the herring fail them. Yet, as I have said, the far-flung fishing industry is affected by the abundance or the scarcity of the brit. When these tiny crustaceans abound, there is a large run of herring; and when the brit is scarce, the herring run is correspondingly small.

Considering that sea birds, vast numbers of herring, countless fish, innumerable marine animals—especially whales—devour the tiny crustaceans, it is amazing that the brit continue to multiply. However, a single Cyclops will produce nearly five billion young in a single year, provided, of course, the prolific creature survives life's hazards for a year. It is indeed fortunate that only one out of millions—or probably one out of billions—of the crustaceans lives for twelve months; otherwise they would soon become so abundant that the sea would be a mass of crustacean jelly. Even as it is, they are so incredibly numerous that in spite of the fact that they are almost transparent, they actually redden many square miles of the surface of the sea at times.

Most of the brit live in ordinary sea water, but certain species prefer brackish water and live in the creeks and estuaries; others are partial to the saltiest brine and survive only where the water is so dense with salt that it is as thick as mud. In some of the Bahamas and other West Indian islands where sea salt is prepared by evaporation under the sun, there are immense "pans" or enclosures in which the water passes through its various stages, the salt becoming more and more concentrated until, in the last pan, it forms crystals of crude salt. In these pans the salt-loving crustaceans gather in enormous numbers, the most numerous being the Cyclops. Even where the water has almost completely disappeared and the crystals of salt are forming, these strange crustaceans thrive by thousands. They are so numerous that the salt harvesters find them a great nuisance and rake them aside in windrows.

If it were not for the flocks of gulls, terns, snipe, willet, and other sea birds that gorge themselves on the one-eyed wiggling crustaceans, they would be even worse. But the birds that destroy the greatest number of the strange creatures are the long-legged pink and scarlet flamingos that stalk about in the shallow water, constantly scooping up the brine in their boat-shaped bills and—as the water drains off—swallowing the crustaceans. So intent are they on gathering the Cyclops that the ordinarily shy birds pay no attention to nearby human beings, and often feed within arm's length of workmen. However, the flamingos sometimes fall victims to their greed. The brine, spattered on their plumage and dripping from their beaks onto their wings, crystallizes and cements their feathers together so that it is impossible for the birds to take flight. Then, frightened and struggling, they fall in the brine and become so covered with salt that they perish. It is a common sight to see numbers of the dead birds lying about, completely encased in salt. Indirectly, the little Cyclops have their revenge and destroy their worst enemies.

Most of the smaller crustaceans are phosphorescent or luminous; there is one species that, for its size, is the most brilliant of all sea creatures. Although a tiny animal, its light is so intense that it is visible even in daylight. Surely, taken all in all, the teeming hordes of brit are among the strangest of all crustaceans.

17

Fishing for Living Lights

THE GLOW of phosphorescent lights in the sea always arouses interest and wonder. At times it is either entirely absent, or only spots of lambent green light are visible in the dark water; at other times the whole sea may appear as if powerful lights were shining upward from its depths. Frequently every wavelet washing on the beach will glow like molten gold, and each ripple on the surface of the sea will be traced in silvery luminescence against the background of translucent green, flecked and dotted with glowing lights. As a rowboat moves through the magic sea, ripples of liquid silver curl from its bow, molten gold drips from the oars, and in its wake it leaves a path of scintillating emerald light. Such is the phosphorescent display at its best.

In some places there is more "fire" in the sea than in others, the light varying in brilliancy and quantity according to the season, temperature of the water, and climatic conditions, and many factors not even understood by scientists. Often, night after night, no phosphorescence will be visible; then, suddenly, the sea will be filled with light. Sometimes in localities where the display is almost as certain as the tides, it may cease abruptly and no sign of the phenomenon will occur for several nights.

That there should be so much variation in the brilliance and extent of the phosphorescence is not surprising, for it is caused by the presence of countless minute marine creatures, each emitting its own luminous glow of some particular color, and, like nearly all of the smaller animals inhabiting the sea, these light-emitting creatures may swarm by thousands in one area at one time or may be wholly absent at another time. No one class of marine life causes the light in the sea; worms, jellyfish, crustaceans, and even some fish are phosphorescent. Also, many of the larval forms of the echinoderms, the corals, the sponges, and other kinds of marine animals emit light, even though it is absent in the adults. Largely, however, the luminosity is caused by the Foraminifera and the brit; the brighter spots and moving lights are jellyfish, marine worms, and fairly good-sized crustaceans.

Some night when the liquid display of fire is at its best, fill a pail with sea water; you will see hordes of small creatures, many of them aglow with colored light. If you dip a fine-mesh scoop net into the sea, you will discover many more light-giving creatures. Fishing for living lights is a fascinating experience and will arouse interest in people ordinarily unimpressed by the wonders of Nature.

On one of my expeditions to the West Indies, our craft was anchored close to a coral reef miles from the nearest of the Bahamas. The phosphorescent display in the calm, crystal-clear water was the most brilliant and beautiful I had ever seen; the sea was fairly aglow with flashing lights, streaks of green, red, and yellow fire, and masses of soft, silvery light. The sailors became interested in the unusual sight and plied me with queries as to what manner of creatures were the cause of the display.

To enable us to see the sources of the light, I had a powerful floodlight lowered over the side; as the light from the thousand-candlepower bulbs penetrated into the sea, an astounding scene was revealed. From the surface down to the limit of the light's rays, the ocean was alive with creatures of countless forms, sizes, and colors. Some moved slowly about or dashed here and there at terrific speed; others spun in dizzy circles like miniature tops or dove and jumped; many appeared to be skating on the surface of the sea.

All of the crew, as well as the captain and mate, had gathered at the rail to watch the aquatic menagerie and circus revealed by the floodlight, but my chief diver, Davis, was most interested; he really became excited and enthusiastic. This was astonishing, for never before had he shown the slightest interest in any phase of natural history. Even when exploring the coral reefs, where we were surrounded by many forms of strange marine life, he had taken it all as a matter of course and had shown no curiosity. But now, as he peered over the ship's side, he was transformed into an amateur naturalist.

"By Jonah!" he exclaimed, "I never knew the ocean was so cram-jam full of the darned bugs. Hey, Professor, look at that critter—looks like a red-hot golf ball. And what's that streaky rope of green fire?" The streaky rope he referred to appeared to be a luminous green snake perhaps ten feet long and several inches in diameter.

"I certainly don't know what the green thing is," I said. "For that matter, I can't identify more than a fraction of the creatures. I suggest we catch some and find out what they are."

Leaning over the rail, Davis dipped a fine-meshed, long-handled scoop net into the brightly lit area, and swinging it on board, dumped the contents into a tub of fresh sea water. Instantly, innumerable points of varicolored light glowed in the tub, and dozens of small creatures dashed back and forth. But there was no sign of diver Davis's "green rope."

"Well, I'll be sunk!" exclaimed the big diver. "Where in blazes did that green thing go to? I know I caught it, but it ain't here." Then, glancing over the side of the ship: "No sign of it out there, neither," he announced.

"It must have escaped," I told him. "It probably shut off its light and dove. It—look, what's that in the net?"

Clinging to the wet net was a long, slender white worm about as thick as a piece of twine. Curious to find out what sort of creature it might be, I dipped the net in the tub and turned it inside out. The result was startling and Davis expressed his amazement with a volley of deep-sea oaths. Apparently filling the tub was the huge, bright-green serpentine creature that had aroused our curiosity.

"I'll be darned," cried the ship's captain who had been gazing at the tub's contents. "Am I seeing things? Where in thunder did that green snake come from?"

"Search me," Davis replied. "I swear it wasn't in the net; now there it is in the tub. Are we *all* seeing things?"

Plunging my hand into the water, I passed it under a loop of the glowing green object and lifted it from the tub.

"There's the solution to the mystery," I announced, as the weird creature vanished, leaving nothing but the stringlike white worm in my grasp.

Davis scratched his head and stared. "That sure beats me," he said. "How do you account for it, Professor?"

"Just the effect of the phosphorescent glow," I explained. "What we saw in the water was the light the worm makes, not its actual body."

"Look what's here!" exclaimed the mate, who had been

peering into the tub. "That's the queerest-looking fish I ever saw."

"Fish!" exclaimed the skipper. "That's no fish; it's a hoptoad."

"It's a mouse-fish," I told them. "Lives in the sargassum weed. See how it's colored exactly like the weed and how its front fins are like feet? If——"

I was interrupted by a peal of laughter from the diver. "Gosh," he cried. "I never seen such funny doodlebugs."

His classification was not far off, for the "doodlebugs" were insects. They were almost exact counterparts of the queer "water boatmen" or "back swimmers" so common in ponds and streams.

"I'll tell you a mighty strange fact about these fellows," I said. "As long as they stay on top of the water and remain upside down, they are safe, but if they are tipped over and get thoroughly wet they'll die."

But Davis's doodlebugs, the lightning-change-artist worm, and the odd fish were only a small portion of the assortment of weird sea creatures in our emergency aquarium. Each time the diver dipped his net in the sea, he added new and even stranger curiosities to our collection. His "red-hot golf ball" was revealed as a globular jellyfish. There were countless wriggling worms of all sizes and shapes, aglow with varicolored light. But most numerous of all were the crustaceans. Many were so transparent that they would have been invisible had it not been for their darker, more opaque internal organs, their black eyes, and the faint bluish glow they emitted. Others resembled small shrimp with extremely long, slender bodies. Still others were stubby-headed creatures that gleamed with blue, green, gold, and scarlet and whose threadlike antennae were six times the length of their bodies.

There were lively "hoppers" decked out in white and crimson, who constantly leaped from the water and secured a toehold on the sides of the bucket several inches above the surface, only to drop back and apparently burst into orange flame as they touched the water.

Most fascinating of all, perhaps, were slender ones, brilliant yellow in color, with huge heads and great goggle eyes. As if overbalanced by the weight of their heads, these odd creatures apparently found it impossible to move in a straight line, and swam rapidly and excitedly in zigzags, curves, and circles, while intensely bright lights flashed from orange spots on their abdomens.

"Look like portholes on a cruise ship," observed Davis. "But something's gone adrift with their steering gear." The luminosity of these various creatures was so intense that they glowed brightly even in the light from the deck lamps. In darkness, the water in the tub held a soft blue-green glow even where there were no signs of living creatures and no moving specks of light. Davis and the others wanted to know what caused it.

"Thousands of minute creatures," I told them. "Living organisms so small they can't be seen by the naked eye; some are the invisible young of many of the creatures we can see."

"By Jonah's black pocket!" Davis ejaculated. "I must have et millions of the blasted critters with all the sea water I've swallered."

"I been thinking those bugs has got it all over us humans," observed the engineer, who had been silently watching our show. "I'd say offhand that every one of 'em has a light as powerful as a thousand-watt bulb, and keeps it goin' without heat, without machinery, and with no chance of breakin' down or burnin' out. Wish I could learn how they do it. I'd be a multimillionaire overnight."

The following morning, when we peered over the ship's side at the sea, there were no signs of the hordes of creatures that had swarmed everywhere during the night. Davis dipped his net in the water, but it came up empty except for a few of the topsy-turvy, back-swimming insects. As I explained to the men, the majority of the light-givers we had studied were inhabitants of the deep sea; with the first signs of daylight they had retired to the darkness of the depths, there to remain until night again shrouded the surface of the sea.

18

Babes in the Sea

BABIES of all kinds are interesting and unpredictable. Perhaps one reason that they are so interesting is that one can never tell what they will be like when they grow up. Even human babies have but little resemblance to grown men and women. A calf is unmistakably a baby cow; kittens, piglets, lambs, puppies, and various other youngsters somewhat resemble their parents. Only a naturalist could distinguish a baby grasshopper, cricket, or cockroach from its parents. But there is scarcely any similarity between a downy chick and a cackling hen or a fuzzy duckling and a quacking duck. If we did not know, we never would suspect that a caterpillar is a baby butterfly, or that a wiggler is an infant mosquito. Just why the young of some creatures should look like the adults and others should not is a mystery that makes babies all the more intriguing. Taken all in all, babies are wonderful, and many of the most wonderful babies are those who live in the sea.

Infant, or larval, forms of many kinds of sea creatures swarm by millions everywhere in the ocean. They are almost as numerous as the brit, and much of the phosphorescence of sea water is caused by these infant sea creatures. Probably nowhere else on earth is the death rate so high as among the young of marine animals. This is fortunate for us, for even if an infinitesimal percentage of the sea creatures' babies lived to maturity, there would not be enough space in the oceans to hold them, nor enough food to feed them; many marine animals are capable of producing millions of young in a few months.

As a rule, the young sea creatures have little or no resemblance to their parents. The metamorphosis of many is as great as in the case of the caterpillar's changing to a butterfly. And the difference in habits is as great as in appearance. Nearly all are lively, free-swimming creatures, even if they become firmly attached to some immovable or movable objects in later life.

In order to watch and enjoy these babes in the sea to the best advantage, a glass dish of sea water should be placed on a black cloth, paper, or other surface; many of the infants are so transparent that they are almost invisible against a white background. A great deal of the numerous creatures usually found in a pail of sea water are invisible except through a microscope; others are so small they should be watched through a good reading glass. But there are plenty that may easily be seen and watched without the use of any lens, and luckily the most interesting baby sea creatures are in this class.

Probably the first object you will notice will be two black specks moving rapidly back and forth in front of a dark, crooked thread. Looking carefully, you will discover that these little objects are surrounded by an almost invisible outline, and that the whole is a tiny, shrimplike creature; the black objects are its eyes and intestine. It is, in fact, an infant shrimp. Next, your attention may be drawn to a very different creature with two tiny black eyes and a slightly bluish body set between two broad, oval, semi-transparent wings fringed with constantly vibrating hairs. Although you might never suspect it, this is actually a baby sea shell.

Not far from that infant is a swiftly moving chap darting here and there with spasmodic jerks and constantly changing its shape. One instant it is almost spherical, the next moment oval, or it may become quite elongated. There is a dark spot on one side and the body is dotted and lined with blue. Internal organs are faintly visible, and at one end there is a ring of long, slender, vibrating hairs. In fact, it looks more like some sort of tiny jellyfish than anything else; but it really is a baby oyster. No wonder it is hurrying about and enjoying itself while it may, for in a few days it will dive to the bottom, fasten itself to some convenient object, develop a hard shell, and become what the oystermen call a "set," or "seed" oyster.

Then another little creature attracts attention. In some ways it resembles the baby oyster, for there are vibratory hairs at one end of the body; but instead of being more or less globular it is conical in outline, and the entire body is fringed with short hairs. Having learned that the other swiftly swimming creatures you have seen are young sea shells you might reasonably assume that this creature is also a baby mollusk. It is, however, the larval form of a marine worm. After a short period of an active swimming life it will bury itself in mud or sand and be transformed into a mature marine worm with a gorgeous array of plumes waving above its head.

I have already told you about the remarkable barnacles and their young. The chances are that there will be a number of these babies in your dish of sea water. If so, you will probably find them in a little group at one side of the dish where they struggle and push one another about as if striving to escape a foe. They are strange-looking

little things, shaped a bit like upside-down boats, with a
tuft of hairs at one end, and five or six tufts of hairs—like
miniature oars—projecting from the underside, and a number of long, very thin, bristle-like tentacles where the head
should be.

Another odd creature has large goggle eyes separated by
a sharp nose, and a slender, jointed abdomen. It swims
swiftly by means of six pairs of brushlike appendages on

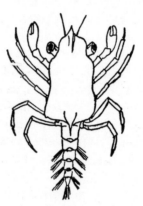

Baby crab

either side. It is far more shrimplike than the baby
shrimps you have seen. This is not so strange, for it is a
baby lobster and, broadly speaking, a lobster is only a
gigantic shrimp.

Very different indeed is another little fellow with a long,
curved horn on its back, a nose like a heron's bill, huge
black eyes, an upturned tail with short spines along its
sides, and jointed legs ending in tufts of hairs. If I should
tell you this is a "megalops," you would not be much
wiser, so I might as well explain that this is the name be-
stowed by scientists on the baby crab in one of its early

stages. It has so little resemblance to adult crabs that for
a long time even the naturalists considered it a distinct
genus of crustacean.

As the megalops grows older and reaches what we call
the walking stage in the case of human babies, it greatly
changes its appearance. It is now obviously a crustacean,
but bears little resemblance to any sort of crab. With an
elongated body, a long, jointed abdomen fringed with

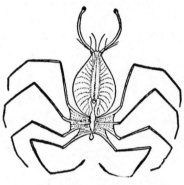

Glass crab

tufts of hairs, a spine for a nose between eyes on stalks,
eight jointed legs, and a pair of nipperlike claws, it looks
like a miniature lobster. But with later changes of its skin,
the elongated thorax will become shorter and broader, as
will the abdomen and the tail, which will be tucked up beneath the body; the creature will be transformed into a
small but recognizable crab.

If you have taken the water in your dish from tropical
or semitropical seas, you will probably discover some beautiful little creatures called "glass crabs" by the fishermen
of Great Britain, where the strange animals are very numerous. It is an appropriate name, for the little fellows are

as shiny and transparent as spun glass. They appear to be made of delicate lace composed of tiny crystals. The long slender legs resemble glass tubes, and their black eyes seem encased in the ends of glass stalks. Like nearly all babies of the sea, these glass crabs change their appearance considerably as they grow. In one stage they have large, beautifully etched bodies with a very small abdomen bordered on both sides by a weblike area connecting the four pairs of extremely thin and delicate legs. At the forward, narrower end of the body are two long, curved stalks terminating in small dark eyes, with fine bristles at the bases.

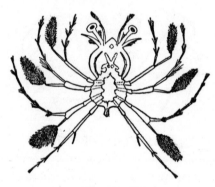

Glass crab

In another stage the long legs are tipped with bunches of bristles and resemble bottle brushes; the body is almost circular in outline, there are four hairy antennae, and the big black eyes are on stout stalks. Until quite recently these glass crabs were an unsolved mystery to zoologists, for no one even suspected that they were the young of the big sea crayfish.

In addition to the babes in the sea I have mentioned already, you will find many others as strange and as puz-

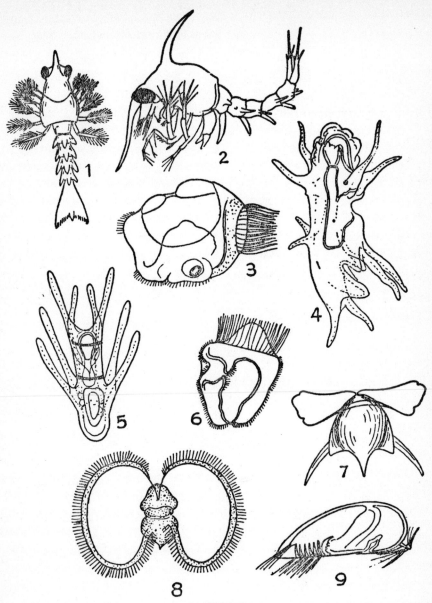

PLATE VII

1. *Young lobster*   2. *Young crab*   3. *Young oyster*   4. *Young star-fish*   5. *Young sea urchin*   6. *Young worm*   7. *Pteropod, a swimming shell*   8. *Young shell*   9. *Young barnacle*

zling. One is a rather long, slender creature, almost like a man in outline, but with four "legs" and four "arms"; it has neither neck nor eyes. It is semi-transparent with numerous dark lines and patches marking its internal anatomy. It swims about freely but slowly. Nobody would ever suspect that this strange creature is a young sea urchin.

An even more remarkable creature, present in sea water almost everywhere, resembles some sort of miniature freak quadruped fit for a sideshow. It has four leglike appendages on one side of its somewhat rectangular body; on what we might consider the head there are two curved "horns"; on the "rump," so to speak, are two additional "horns," and there are two fleshy "tails." Its conspicuous eye, instead of being in the head, is in the base of one of the leglike appendages. Through its slightly opaque body its internal organs are plainly to be seen. It swims about quite rapidly, using its "legs" as fins, and constantly shrinking and swelling in a most remarkable manner. It is a baby starfish.

In addition to all these young sea creatures there probably will be infant corals, or zooids, young gorgonians, sponges, and sea anemones. If, after you have watched and studied all the visible creatures in your dish, you should empty it and dip up a fresh lot of sea water, the chances are you would find it filled with numbers of tiny creatures you had not previously seen. Everywhere the tiny denizens of the sea are constantly changing. At one time in one area, certain forms of life will abound; in the same spot at another time, totally different creatures may swarm. At different stages of the tides there will be different forms of life; on warm days the sea creatures will be quite unlike those found in the same locality on cold days. The young forms of the innumerable species of marine animals multiply endlessly and—to make them all the more interesting and confusing—these babes in the sea are continually changing their appearance with age and the approach of maturity and a sedentary life.

19

Crabs: Hermits and Soldiers

THERE is an old saying: "When doctors disagree, who can decide?" The same is true of zoologists and other scientists, and there are many sea creatures that cause the most erudite naturalists to disagree.

This is particularly true of the crustaceans. No sooner do the scientists work out a system of classification than some creature bobs up that has the characteristics of two or more forms combined, or else lacks the essential features it should have to fit into the scheme of things. The squilla—or mantis shrimp—already described, the flat lobster—or sea cockroach—and several members of the Crustacea are scientific misfits. Since the zoologists could not decide whether these outsiders belonged in one group or another, they solved the problem by creating special families, often with only one species, to accommodate the puzzling creatures.

But there are a number remaining which are still betwixts and betweens. According to scientific classification, and omitting minor anatomical differences, the lobster has an elongated thorax, or carapace, a long and segmented abdomen, and a flat tail, made up of hinged plates to serve as a swimming aid. The crab, on the other hand, has a

rounded carapace; the tail, short and broad, is kept tucked
beneath the body, where it fits into a special groove; swimming is accomplished by means of the legs, and the crab
moves sideways, instead of backwards like the lobster.
But numerous decapod crustaceans do not completely ful-
fill the requirements of either a crab or a lobster.

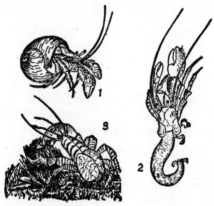

1. Hermit crab
2. Hermit crab without shell
3. Coconut crab

The commonest and best known of these misfits are the
hermit crabs—active, amusing little creatures who take
possession of empty sea shells and scurry about carrying
their houses on their backs. As long as the hermit crab
remains at home and allows only his head, shoulders, feet,
and claws to be seen, he has all the earmarks of a crab.
But if we remove the interesting chap from his shell apartment, we will find that his crablike appearance ends at
his waist, or where his thorax and abdomen join. Back of
this, the little fellow has a soft, curved body unprotected
by plates or a hard skin and so translucent that the in-

testinal tract is visible. At the extreme end of the abdomen are two small horny hooks which are metamorphosed and highly specialized legs.

At first sight the hermit crab appears to possess only three pairs of legs on each side, two of which end in sharp tips and are used in walking, while the third pair are greatly enlarged and are provided with powerful nippers. But if you look carefully you will find the missing pair of legs tucked in back of the walking legs. In other words, the hermit minus its house more closely resembles a soft-bodied lobster than a true crab, and so, to be on the safe side, the zoologists have made the hermit crabs a distinct tribe of crustaceans called *Paguridae*.

Few sea creatures are so perfectly adapted to the life they lead as are the hermit crabs. Whether Nature designed them to occupy empty shells or whether it was an acquired habit, the zoologists cannot say. But if some remote ancestor of these creatures tucked its tail into an empty shell and found safety there and its descendants followed the example, each succeeding generation would become more and more adapted to the shell-dwelling habit. Try to drag a hermit crab from its borrowed shell and you will be amazed to find that the little chap will permit itself to be torn apart before it will release its hold. How, you may wonder, does the creature obtain such a grip on the smooth internal surface of the shell?

The secret lies in the strangely altered legs near the tip of the abdomen, which have been transformed into short hooks serving as anchors, and the short, stout, hook-tipped fifth pair of legs with which it grips the shell just within the aperture. Also, the body of the crab is coiled to exactly fit the interior of the shell it occupies. Although able to retain possession of its acquired house, the hermit takes no chances of being forcibly evicted and, at the first sign of danger, draws into the shell and tightly closes the front door.

The crab's claws differ greatly, one being large and broad, the other much smaller. If you examine a number of the creatures you will discover that the majority are right-handed—that is, the right-hand claw is the larger one. You may wonder why the two claws are so different in size and shape. If you examine a hermit that has withdrawn into its shell you will notice the crab's claws are its folding doors. The larger claw covers the greater part of the opening of the shell, while the small claw fits neatly into the aperture left by the big claw and locks the latter into place.

Moreover, the relative sizes, as well as the shapes of the claws, vary greatly in different species of hermit crabs; each type of claw is suited to the aperture of the particular type of shell the crab selects for its residence. To be sure, just the right sort of shell may not be available when the crab grows too large for its apartment and decides to move into larger quarters, and he may be forced to take possession of a different type of shell. When that happens it is only a temporary measure, and the moment the uncomfortable crab finds the right sort of shell, he moves in.

Possibly, countless ages ago, all hermit crabs had claws exactly alike and were satisfied with any sort of shell, just as in the distant past human beings were satisfied with any sort of a house or shelter. Tastes, however, vary among crabs as well as among human beings, and the ancestors of today's hermit crabs found certain types of shells more satisfactory for their needs than other types. But unlike humans, who can make their residences conform to their tastes and comfort, the crabs were forced to make themselves conform to the peculiarities of their acquired homes.

Those species customarily dwelling in wide-mouthed shells gradually developed broad, heavy claws with which to close the aperture. Others, who had a taste for shells with a narrow opening, developed claws that would fit the doorway. There were even crabs who, for one reason or another, thought that the tusklike *Dentalium* and long, tapered *Terebra* shells were ideal homes. Today you will find many of these occupied by hermits with one circular claw that just fits the shell's aperture, while the other claw is so small that it is tucked inside with the other feet.

You may wonder why so many hermits are right-handed. The reason is that the majority of sea shells are "dextral," or right-handed, and through centuries of adaptation, the majority of the hermit crabs have become right-handed to accommodate themselves to the right-handed shells. If you look at a sea shell with the opening toward you, the aperture will be on the right-hand side and the spiral whorls at the top of the shell will go from right to left. Occasionally there will be a freak shell that is the reverse, or left-handed, and certain species are naturally left-handed, or "sinistral." In areas where there are natural left-handed shells, you will find a great many left-handed crabs. There are some species of hermit crabs who are not satisfied with their claw doors as protection, but fence themselves in with the rows of sharp, pointed spines along the edges of their claws.

Since these crabs grow rapidly and their acquired sea shells remain the same size, the hermits are frequently forced to move into larger and larger shells; finally, having reached their full size, they can remain in their shell-houses, until they are worn out from continual dragging over sand and rocks.

It is a most interesting and amusing sight to watch a hermit crab when moving day arrives. Hurrying about, the little fellow examines every empty shell he can find, inspecting each with his alert, stalked eyes, feeling it with his long, sensitive antennae, turning it this way and that. If the exterior of the shell satisfies him, he will thrust his antennae or an exploratory claw into it. Finally, having found one that seems exactly suited to his needs, he will slip out of his old house and pop into the new one so swiftly that the change of domicile is barely visible. Then, wiggling his abdomen about, drawing himself in, and trying out his claws for a door, he will give the newly acquired home a thorough test. If all is quite satisfactory he will go tiptoeing off about his business. But if for any reason the new shell is not entirely to his liking, he will continue on his house-hunting travels until he finds one that is just right.

Seldom is the house-hunting crab satisfied with his first selection. His requirements are far more exacting than those of any house-hunting human being. The shell he is to occupy until his next move must be exactly the right size and shape, large enough to allow for his growth and yet small enough to hold securely and to block the opening effectually with his claws. And since his soft, fleshy abdomen has acquired the twist of his previous shell, he must, if possible, find a new shell with the same internal spiral chambers as the old one. He will try to select a shell of the same species as the one he has outgrown, for even if the interior of another species is much the same and his body will eventually adjust itself, it will be very uncomfortable for some time. Apparently the droll little crabs have their individual tastes in architecture and decorations, for frequently a hermit crab will vacate a newly acquired and apparently satisfactory shell to take possession of a more brightly colored or more perfect specimen of the same species, or a shell that is decorated with tufts of seaweed, small barnacles, or Bryozoa.

When two or more crabs decide to move into the same shell, the hermits' house-hunting often ends in battle. Each claims priority and will fight viciously, biting with the powerful claws, striving to drag the opponent from the safety of his shells, and biting off antennae and legs. The struggle will continue until one has been defeated and the triumphant but usually battle-scarred victor takes possession of the shell he has won.

The hermit crabs are lively, sociable creatures constantly scurrying about as if their lives depended upon their getting somewhere in a hurry, although they never seem to arrive at any particular destination. They remind one of the hurrying crowds of human beings pushing, jostling, and dashing madly in a New York subway.

There is scarcely a spot along our shores where the hermits are not abundant. Mud flats, sand bars, beaches, tide pools, rock crevices, masses of seaweed, spaces beneath stones or other objects—all are popular haunts. The crabs are nearly all little fellows running about bearing the shells of small winkles, drills, and *Litorina*. But there are species of hermit crabs in deeper water that grow to immense size—real giants with powerful claws several inches across, occupying huge conch, triton, and whelk shells that weigh several pounds each. In the north, all of the hermit crabs are sea-dwellers or inhabit the damp sand or mud at the edge of the sea, but in the tropics there are many that dwell on land many miles from the ocean. One often finds them high in the mountains of South America and the West Indies; it is a strange and incongruous sight to come upon a big sea shell being carried about by a crab in the jungle. These "soldier crabs," as they are called, are of all sizes from infant chaps to veterans with two- or three-inch claws who carry small conch shells or massive pearly turban shells on their backs.

As a rule they are scattered, but in certain areas they are numerous and sometimes become real pests, entering houses and camps and dining on whatever they consider edible, which includes almost everything that human beings eat. They even will crawl into beds on their exploratory visits, and it is a sound sleeper indeed who will not awaken instantly when a soldier crab tiptoes over his face or body, a heavy shell bumping along behind, and antennae and claws investigating his ears and nose as if considering the possibility of a permanent residence. The larger crabs raid hen houses and devour chicks; they also climb trees to eat birds' eggs and nestlings.

Although these soldier crabs are strictly land dwellers, they must deposit their eggs in salt water, where the young crabs are hatched and spend their babyhood. Moreover, the sea is the only source of the shells that the soldier crabs must have each year as they outgrow their old shells. Strangely enough the urge to move to the sea to lay eggs and acquire new shells affects all of the land hermits at the same time. It becomes a mass mania, and instead of heading seaward singly or in small groups, they gather from far and near and, forming a vast army of thousands of crabs, they march onward toward the distant ocean. It is for this reason they are called "soldier crabs," and anyone who ever has seen the crustaceans on their annual trek will realize how appropriate is the name.

For months a person may dwell in the bush and never encounter more than a few dozen crabs in a day, but when the migratory time arrives they suddenly appear in droves, seemingly materializing from nowhere, and all moving in the same general direction as if summoned to some definite spot. As the thousands of crabs move onward, each trundling a sea shell on its back, they present a wonderful spectacle. To be sure, they are not in very close formation and even though open spaces occur between the columns of moving crabs, the army may extend for miles. The rustling of their legs over dry leaves and grass and the clinking of their shells against stones and fallen tree limbs, make a racket, especially during the night when they are the most active.

Once they are on the march and headed for the shore nothing but fire will stop their onward march. Trees, walls, and even high precipices will be climbed. If they reach some impenetrable or insurmountable barrier they will detour, often traveling several miles in order to get around the obstacle, but invariably, unerringly maintaining their original direction once they can continue onward. If they relied upon a compass to guide them they could not follow a more direct course; if the crabs are caught and turned around, they instantly turn back for the sea the moment they are released. Even if they are carried miles inland and placed in a district entirely new to them, they invariably head for the nearest shore.

The marching crabs travel steadily and without rest, night and day. They may be compelled to march for many miles, and several weeks may pass between the time the march starts and the time the army arrives at the shore. Some may live within a short distance of the sea, yet all arrive at the same time; those close to the water wait for the crabs from farther away and then join the surging, onward march.

Once the crabs arrive at their destination, the "soldiers" break ranks to scatter here and there; although the sandy beaches and rocky shores may swarm for days with the big, the small, and the medium-sized crabs, there is no real army, no organized mass. Each one is seeking food for itself and is busily occupied in searching for a new and larger shell. One might suppose that there would soon be a dearth of suitable empty shells to accommodate the thousands of soldier crabs. But they never are troubled by the housing problem. Thousands of the outgrown shells are discarded. These are of all sizes, and only the very largest crabs require fresh shells; on tropical shores there seldom is any lack of dead shells cast up on the beach.

Having finally acquired a new home, each crab takes to the water and has a glorious time in the salty sea. When the females have deposited their eggs and all the crabs have changed their skins and moved into new shells, the homeward trek begins. There is no army on the return trip. The crabs travel inland singly and in small groups; they follow no direct route but wander about, stopping here and there, sometimes taking up a permanent residence in a new locality, until once more all are scattered far and wide.

These land hermit crabs make unusual pets and are quite intelligent. At one time I kept a number of them confined in a glass jar for nearly a year. They thrived on a diet of fresh green vegetables, fruit, and chopped meat. They changed their shells a number of times. It was really amazing to see how intelligent they were, for I never had suspected that crabs had brains and the power of reasoning. For a time the hermits would draw into their shells and close their claw-doors when anyone approached, but soon they became so accustomed to us that they would even eat food from our fingers. However, if a stranger came near they would instantly lock themselves into their shells. Like other creatures, they varied greatly in intelligence.

One large female would answer to a certain whistle; she would wave her antennae—obviously listening—and scurry to the side of the jar when she heard the signal. She loved to be taken out and petted; she would nestle down in my wife's hand to enjoy being stroked. She never tried to nip with her powerful claws, but used them as supplementary legs and crawled about over our hands and arms. Eventually, when the annual call of the sea came, the tame hermits refused to eat and became restless and uneasy. So we carried them to the beach where hundreds of their fellows were having an aquatic moving day, and released them.

Although the soldier crabs, as well as the more familiar salt-water hermit crabs, dwell in empty sea shells, there are some species that prefer sponges or even the hollow stalks of marine plants. One group of hermit crabs never bothers to acquire a protective covering but goes about with abdomens exposed. These are gigantic creatures found in the Pacific islands and known as "robber crabs" or "coconut crabs." Instead of the soft, fleshy abdomen of ordinary hermits, these huge crustaceans have the abdomen protected by a tough, leathery skin, and the tail is kept tucked under the body in the manner of a true crab. In these monsters, all of the legs are fully developed; the last pair terminates in small but strong claws; the next three have sharp, pointed toes; the forward pair bear huge and very powerful claws.

These robber crabs climb trees as readily as do the soldier crabs and their favorite food is the coconut. It may seem an impossibility for even these monstrous crabs to tear away the tough husk of a coconut and crack open the hard shell. But they find no difficulty in accomplishing the task; they are tremendously strong and can easily strip off the fibrous outer covering of the nuts and get at the meat. Some idea of their strength may be gained by the fact that these crabs, when placed in an empty kero-

sene tin, have no trouble escaping by puncturing and tearing away the metal. When free their principal food
consists of coconuts, but in captivity they refuse to eat
them, preferring carrion, especially dead rats. The robber
crabs use the fibre of the coconut husks as lining for their
burrows as well as for food.

Although they never travel in armies, their habits are
similar to those of the soldier crabs. They too are obliged
to enter the sea once a year in order to deposit their eggs,
but, in addition, they cannot live unless they enter the
water at least once a day to dampen their gills. And like
the soldier crabs, they often enter houses. They have won
the name of robber crab because of their thieving nature;
they are inveterate kleptomaniacs. Books, magazines,
shoes, clothing, dishes, cutlery—even clocks, watches, and
ammunition—are all carried off by these crabs during the
nighttime. Although the ten-legged thieves often abandon
the useless stolen objects, they have a most annoying habit
of carrying the loot into the tree tops, where it cannot be
found by the unfortunate victims of the robber crabs' raids.

20

Crabs: Soft-Shells and Hardbacks

To DEALERS in sea foods, proprietors of restaurants, and those who are fond of the succulent crustaceans, the edible crabs of our coasts are divided into two classes—the soft-shells, or shedders, and the hardbacks. But to our British cousins, "fishmongers," and the public, crabs are crabs, and the soft-shelled crabs are seldom eaten. On our side of the Atlantic, the blue crabs are the only widely consumed kind; but in England, as well as in Cuba and elsewhere in the tropics, rock crabs are the favorite, and shedder rock crabs are seldom seen or captured.

In Chapter 12, I described how lobsters shed their shells; crabs change their outer coverings in a different manner. The outgrown horny skin of the lobster splits open along the back; that of the crab opens along a seam from side to side at the rear end of the body. Unlike the lobsters, who seek refuge in holes or beneath stones during the time when their new shells are soft, the common blue crabs remain in the open; their new shells harden rapidly. Within twenty-four hours a true "soft-shell" crab will become a "shedder"; a few days later it will be a "hardback."

The rock crabs—or stone crabs, as they are also called —follow the example of the lobsters and remain concealed until their new shells are thoroughly hard. Thus, although shedder blue crabs are taken by thousands and are familiar to all who eat crabs, the shedder rock crabs are practically unknown to most people.

Crabs vary in size from tiny creatures less than an inch across the back to monsters with a span of several feet

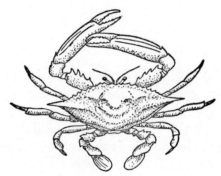

Swimming crab

from leg-tip to leg-tip; in tropical seas there are species with a spread of nearly ten feet. Regardless of size, color, or edibility, all the countless species of crabs are scientifically divided into two main groups known as the swimming crabs and the walking crabs; the latter are divided into a number of tribes and family groups such as the box crabs, rock crabs, mud crabs, and spider crabs. There are also a number that the scientists do not consider true crabs but as links between the crabs and other crustaceans.

Our most popular edible crabs are the blue crabs of the swimming crab group. The members of this group have the last pair of legs terminating in the thin, oval paddles which make these crabs rapid swimmers. Another common member of the group, found from the tropics to New England, is the "lady crab." In the North this species is seldom or never eaten, but in the South it is a highly prized table crab and is considered far superior to the blue crab. It is a very handsome creature, its buff-colored or pinkish shell covered with red or purplish ring-shaped markings; whereas the blue crab, as its name implies, is usually pale blue varied with green, its claws being marked with deep

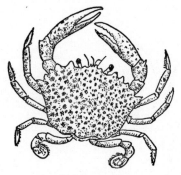

Lady crab

purplish blue. But there are a number of species of the blue crab group—all equally delicious eating—that are far more brightly colored. One is russet-red with claws and markings of deep crimson; another is green with purple claws; still another is brilliant blue with mauve and maroon claws and markings.

All of these "blue crabs" are extremely active, voracious, and pugnacious creatures which dart swiftly through the water, lifting their powerful claws threateningly when cornered, and capturing fishes on which they feed—although, like all crabs, they are as fond of carrion as fresh meat. The lady crab is also a true swimming crab, but its habits are totally unlike those of the blue crab group. Instead of being constantly on the move, this crab burrows into the sand below low-water mark with only its antennae and eyes visible, ready to snap up with incredible speed any passing creature that comes within reach of its powerful claws. Unlike the blue crabs, which either seek safety in flight or boldly attack when danger threatens, the lady crabs, if alarmed, simply bury themselves more deeply until completely out of sight. If by chance they are uncovered they are as courageous and fight as savagely as their blue cousins.

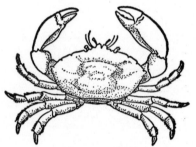

Walking crab

Bravery is one of the most universal and outstanding characteristics of all crabs. Even the little mud and rock crabs found under stones will show fight, rearing on their legs and waving their claws menacingly when faced by a human being—who, of course, looks like a moving mountain to the valiant little chaps. But the bravest of creatures must at times bow to superior power, and when a crab finds itself a captive, unable to frighten or fight its foe, it tries to escape by dropping off a leg or two or even its claws, for Nature provides crabs with special devices for amputating their limbs. A wily crab will leave its leg in the grip of its foe and scuttle away before the captor fully realizes what has happened.

As might be expected, such born warriors fight fiercely among themselves. They seem to go about carrying chips on their shoulders. No armor-clad knight of old was ever better equipped for hand-to-hand fighting. Compared to their size, their hard shells are far more efficient than the steel armor of mediaeval days, and their powerful claws are more effective weapons in crabdom than broadswords were in their time. Of course they have no chance against human foes or large fish, but they never turn tail and run away. Still threatening with their claws, they will move slowly backwards to the safety of some rock crevice.

The battles among themselves may result from any one of a number of causes. One crab may trespass on another's personal territory; two or more may discover some tidbit at the same time and fight for its possession; or they may fight with maniacal fury over a female. At times they appear to engage in a battle for the sheer devil of it. In a group of hundreds of crabs living peacefully side by side, two members of the colony will suddenly engage in a duel for no apparent reason, battling furiously until one or both are too seriously maimed to continue or until they are utterly exhausted. Such combats are seldom duels to the death, however. The fighters may be badly mangled; they may lose claws, legs, antennae, or eyes in the scrap; but even if such crippling injuries render the wounded crab *hors de combat* for a time, the condition is only temporary. With his next change of skin he will appear with all his legs, claws, and other appendages replaced with ones as good or better than those he lost.

Probably the most courageous and "fightingest" crab for its size is the little green crab found everywhere along our eastern shores from Virginia to Cape Cod. Barely two inches across its green and yellow back, this doughty warrior will face a human being and fight with never a thought of retreat. So astonishingly courageous is this crab that he has been given the name *Maenas*, or "frenzied." These little "mad crabs," as the French call them, cannot inflict any real injury on a person, but the big rock crabs are a different proposition. In southern waters they grow to enormous size; the Cuban Morro crab frequently weighing twelve or fifteen pounds, with such huge claws that the meat contained in one is a meal for the average person. Such monsters could easily crush a man's hand; they have no difficulty in crushing the large turban and top shells or the medium-sized conch shells on which they usually feed.

In our northern waters the rock crabs do not reach the proportion of the Morro crabs, but their claws are powerful and they crack and crush clams, whelks, oysters, and other sea shells with ease. In many localities they are considered pests by the lobstermen, for frequently their traps will be filled with rock crabs. They are as good to eat as the blue crabs, but for some unknown reason they are usually considered worthless and the lobstermen toss them on the shore to die, thus wasting many pounds of nutritious meat.

Fiddler crabs are familiar to nearly everyone who has visited muddy areas of shore or the tidewater salt marshes. The male has an enlarged claw which he holds in a pose suggesting a violinist. They are considered one of the best baits for salt water fishing; thousands are captured and sold for this purpose. Unlike the majority of crabs, the fiddlers are vegetarians, and as fighters they are the exception that proves the rule. They are timid creatures who rush at full speed for their burrows at the first sign of danger; they will use their big claws only in self-defense. In still another respect the fiddlers are at variance with other crabs, for they hibernate in their burrows during the cold winter weather.

In this country we never think of fiddlers as edible, but in Europe they are in great demand, especially in Portugal. Since the large claw is the only portion eaten, the thrifty Portuguese crab-gatherers merely break off that claw and release the creature. Thus they conserve the supply of crab claws, for with the next change of skin there will be another crop of claws to be had for the taking.

If you have ever paid any particular attention to the hurrying hordes of fiddler crabs, you may have noticed that the males are all right-handed—that is, the big claw is on the right-hand side. Left-handed fiddlers have been found, but they are as rare as hens' teeth. However, even left-handed fiddler crabs are not as rare as fiddlers with two large claws; only a few such freaks have been found.

A near relative of the fiddler, common on our beaches from the Carolinas southward, is known as the ghost crab. This pale, active crab appears and vanishes in true ghostly fashion. Ghost crabs are very timid, and either dash madly for their burrows in the sand when alarmed or hastily squat motionless; since they are colored exactly like the sand, they become almost invisible. The ghosts may wander about the beaches during the daytime, but they are most numerous during the late afternoon and the night. When the tide is out they often travel long distances from their burrows, but they can run with such amazing speed that it is next to impossible for a man to overtake them. If the crab finds that his pursuer is gaining, it will dart abruptly in some other direction holding its body high, dodging, twisting, and turning with amazing speed but always getting nearer to its hole. Reaching its refuge, the crab will vanish. It is useless to try to dig out the speedy fellow, for the ghost crab can burrow much faster than a man can excavate in the sand. If it finds itself hard-pressed, it will burrow to the surface some distance away and go scuttling off while the pursuer's attention is concentrated on digging.

It is fascinating to watch one of these crabs at work on a burrow, but if you wish to do so, you must remain absolutely motionless. No sea creature has eyes sharper than the ghost crab, and your slightest movement—even a turn of your head—will send the crab into its hole. Keep your eyes fixed on the nearest burrow and you will notice a slight movement of the sand about it. Then two black eyes will appear, looking like miniature periscopes at the tips of their stalks. Having satisfied itself that no enemy is near, the crab will slip out of its home, carrying a little load of sand held close to its body by its legs. It will move several inches from the hole before dumping the burden and ·then raise itself on tiptoe to peer about before disappearing underground, only to reappear with another load of sand.

A crab may work for hours bringing the tiny loads of sand to be added to the dump-pile, until the hole is deep enough to satisfy its needs. If it is merely house cleaning or enlarging the burrow, it may bring out only a few loads. In either case, when the task is completed it will carefully level off the accumulated pile of sand he has dumped, leaving no trace of the telltale hummock.

Its labors completed, the crab will go hunting for a well-earned meal. Making short, quick runs, it will halt abruptly, rear up and peer about. If it happens to see any prey, it completely changes behavior. Crouching close to the sand, the body almost indistinguishable from the surroundings, the crab will move slowly and cautiously forward, stalking his prey like a cat. When within leaping distance of the quarry, the crab will gather its legs beneath it and spring like a miniature tiger upon a sand hopper.

Seldom indeed does the ghost crab fail to bring down its prey, whether it is a buzzing fly, a sluggish isopod, a tiny crab, or some beetle or earwig. He is not at all particular as to what he eats as long as it is taken alive, for everything that he can capture is "game." However, he is not averse to dining on any tidbits of picknickers' lunches or other edibles he may find, and if all else fails he will eat dead creatures cast up by the waves.

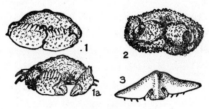

1, 1a. Bashful crab
2. Fortress crab
3. Shield-bearer

Another strange member of the crab family is the box, or bashful, crab, which is found from Cape Hatteras southward. With their high, rounded, boxlike shell and short legs, these crabs give the impression of being clumsy and sluggish, but if alarmed they will show astonishing speed both in running and swimming. They are handsome crabs with a pale pink or yellow shell, decorated with spots and streaks of lilac and red. Their most unusual features are the claws and front legs, which are broad and flat, with a notched upper edge, something like a rooster's comb.

These are strong and powerful nippers, but instead of using them as a means of defense when in danger, the box crab quickly draws its legs beneath its body, where each fits snugly into a depression. Then it folds its broad front legs and claws in front of its face, locking the joints of the claws together. With only its eyes showing, the crab seems overcome with bashfulness. In this position it loses all semblance of a crustacean and might easily be mistaken for an old sea shell. The deception is made all the more perfect when the crab is rolled about by wavelets or currents without showing a sign of life. The strong carapace and protective claws prevent it from being injured; it may be buffeted by the surf or even washed ashore without damage. The moment the crab feels that danger is past it unlocks its claws, unfolds its legs and scurries back into the sea. The claws have another and perhaps more important use. When it burrows in mud, the claws, folded in front of the mouth, serve as a strainer to keep silt and sand from entering its gills.

Like all other crabs, the box crabs shed their shells, but instead of hiding away until the new coverings are hard, they depend upon a fellow crab to protect them in their helpless condition. Where these crabs are common in shallow water one may often see shedders resting on the bottom; close beside each there will be a hard-shelled fellow box crab acting as a bodyguard, ready to battle to the death to protect the shedder.

Another interesting species, found along our southern coasts where there are mangrove trees, are large, gaudily colored crabs with shining black shells and vivid orange or scarlet legs and claws. Dwelling among the mangroves, they climb over the roots and branches in such numbers that, as they scuttle over the oysters clustered on the trees' roots, they make such a noise one might think some large creature were crashing through the swamp. These mangrove crabs are courageous chaps who will fight viciously when cornered, but they believe that discretion is the bet-

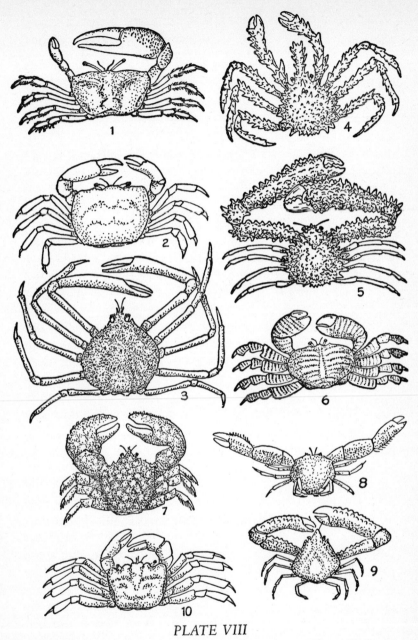

PLATE VIII

1. *Fiddler crab*   2. *Ghost crab*   3. *Spider crab*   4. *The crab that is not a crab*   5. *A strong-arm crab*   6. *Grapsus crab*   7, 8. *The in-between crabs*   9. *Coral crab*   10. *Mangrove crab*

ter part of valor, and either dash back of the tree trunks or dive into the water when danger threatens.

Somewhat similar to these mangrove crabs in habits, but differing greatly in appearance, are the *Grapsus* crabs. These fellows haunt rocky shores, sea walls, docks and wharves. They are flat, brightly colored with red, purple and orange and oddly marked with spots and stripes of lighter colors. Their flat shells and claws, their striped backs, and their habit of crawling over perpendicular rocks and walls—stopping now and again to peer about— gives them a rather loathsome appearance.

But they are timid creatures and about the most defense- less of all crabs, for their shells are paper-thin and their formidable-looking claws too weak to pinch a man's finger hard enough to cause pain. They never show fight; they will wave their claws threateningly, but the gesture is mere bluff. When in danger they rush to hiding places or dive into the water.

Unlike most crabs, the *Grapsus* is obsessed with an in- ordinate curiosity. If a person sits quietly in a spot where they abound, they will come cautiously from their hiding places, creep nearer and nearer to the strange human, and even crawl over the person's body and enter his pockets, apparently trying to discover what this creature is. But at the slightest motion—the drawing of a deep breath, or the twitch of a finger—the crabs will flee in panic, stum- bling over one another in their mad desire to escape.

All along our coasts, ugly-looking spider crabs are com- mon; they make themselves a nuisance to the lobstermen by getting into the traps and eating the bait. No one ever thinks of eating spider crabs, but their meat—what there is of it—is tender and sweet. The very popular tinned Japanese crabmeat is that of spider crabs. However, the Japanese variety are gigantic; they are the largest of all crabs, sometimes measuring ten feet or more across their outstretched legs, and their front legs are as thick as a man's arm. They are caught in especially made traps and are lashed to bamboo frames for transportation. Although the ordinary spider crab has very little meat in its shell, and that mainly in the legs, the giant Japanese crabs' legs contain several pounds of meat each. As an eight- or ten-foot crab would provide enough meat for several families, the Japanese cook their huge crabs in sections and sell them in the markets by the "joint," or leg.

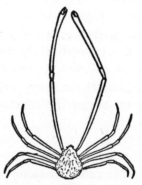

The giant Japanese crab

At one time practically all of the tinned Japanese crab-meat was obtained from giant spider crabs of the seas about Japan and Korea, but in time the big fellows became scarce. Then someone remembered that giant crabs could be found in the Straits of Magellan. Soon dozens of Japanese canneries and villages dotted the shores of the famous straits at the tip of South America, where a species of crab, with even more meat than the giant spider crab, fairly swarm in the ice-cold water.

Although our ordinary spider crabs are slow-moving creatures with small, rather weak claws, there are species with huge front legs armed with enormous, powerful claws used to crush large sea shells. Such crabs, if of gigantic size, would be a real menace to human beings. But these are puny creatures compared to a Tasmanian crab with a body seldom more than a foot in width, but whose claws are three feet in length, and is known to have killed and devoured human beings.

Probably a strong, active man in perfect health could drive off or evade one or even several of these man-eating crabs, but a shipwrecked mariner or castaway, weakened by privations, struggles and hunger, would fall an easy victim to the voracious Tasmanians. For that matter, even the strongest of men armed with adequate weapons would stand little chance if attacked by hundreds of the huge-clawed creatures on the beach of an uninhabited isle.

Taken altogether, crabs occur in more strange forms and fantastic features than any other group of animals. There are some species that closely resemble turtles; there is a Pacific coast crab known as the shield-bearer, whose broad, ridged, convex carapace completely covers the legs and feet like a shield, so that the crab is, in effect, a miniature living armored tank. Even the creature's eyes and head are thoroughly protected by the coat-of-mail, for the forward end of the shield extends in a rectangular section having a narrow slit through which the crab can raise its eyes and peer about as though they were periscopes.

Even stranger in some respects is another crab-resident of our Pacific shores; this fellow is not only capable of transforming itself into a living fortress, but uses air-conditioning. At the joints of both the claws and the next pair of legs, there are semicircular openings appearing to have no great importance as the crab wanders about on the bottom of the sea—a big, powerful, ponderous creature weighing eight or ten pounds, with a spiny body a foot or more

in diameter. Big as it is, it has many enemies. At the first
sign of danger it shuts up tighter than an oyster. Bending
the legs under the body, folding the big saw-toothed claws
together to form a tight door blocking the opening between its back and the folded legs, the big crab is
transformed into an almost spherical fortress. Now the
openings in the crab's leg joints come into play; they serve
as ventilating shafts through which the locked-up crab is
able to breathe.

If you are searching for strange sea creatures under
stones or on rocky shores of our Atlantic coast you may
come upon some small crabs that are tough-looking chaps,
for their huge flattened claws are out of all proportion to
the body. These are known as the strong-armed crabs.
Even if they grew to large size they would be harmless, for they are flaccid, loose-jointed creatures whose
dangerous-appearing claws will fall off at a touch. Scientifically speaking, they are most interesting crustaceans.
They are not true crabs, but are one of the many in-
betweens that connect the lobster and shrimp groups with
the crabs.

Of all the crabs and near-crabs I have seen or heard
about, the most remarkable was a species of huge spider
crab that I obtained in very deep water off the little island
of Dominica in the British West Indies. They were real
giants, three or four feet across, with large nipper claws
and beautiful shades of yellow, red and purple. But their
most remarkable feature was that they were actuated
by hydraulic power—that is, their every movement was
wholly dependent upon water pressure.

Aside from their gills, digestive organs and layers of
muscles within the carapace, there was not an ounce of
meat anywhere. Nowhere within the long, strong legs or
the heavy, powerful claws was there a trace of muscle—

only strong tendons connected to all the joints and joined at their bases to the muscle bands within the body. All motions were controlled by the body muscles and tendons, and only when filled with water under terrific pressure, rendering them rigid, could the legs be operated. Once the pressure was reduced the big crabs were helpless and flaccid, unable even to lift a leg.

21

Crabs: Funny Faces

WITH few exceptions, the hundreds of species of crabs have shell surfaces made up of little elevations and depressions, lines, creases, and pits. It happens that these irregularities of the carapace form lifelike "funny faces," often as grotesque as any man-made mask. I doubt if one person in a thousand who has seen or handled crabs has ever noticed these amusing faces on the creatures' backs; but once they are pointed out, one wonders why one has failed to note them previously.

I once mentioned these "crabby faces" to a friend who had a wayside stand where he sold curios, sea shells, and novelties to tourists. Picking up a crab shell, he stared at it for a moment and chuckled. "Now why didn't I ever notice that before?" he exclaimed. "I'll bet there's money in these things." Gathering quantities of various kinds, he used them in making novelties. Once their funny faces were pointed out to his customers, his crab-back items sold like hotcakes, and in a short time he was keeping several employees busy gathering crabs, cleaning and preparing the shells, and making the novelties.

Nearly all crabs have some sort of funny face on their backs, and no two species have the same one. Hence the variety is almost endless. The highly prized blue crab has an amusing face with a wrinkled forehead, goggle-eyes, and pursed lips framed by a moustache and goatee. The common rock crab's face has beetling brows, puffy cheeks, and a severe mouth, but the Jonah crab wears an elderly, smiling face. The little green crab that scuttles about among the stones, dead shells, and weeds along our shores has a most amusing face on its back; it looks like a freckle-faced girl with rouged cheeks and a fancy hair-do.

One of the common crabs of Europe is known as the "masked" crab. The face upon its back looks like a "sour-puss" with a big bulbous nose, a long upper lip, and a slit-like mouth drawn down at the corners. Incidentally, the masked crab is a remarkable creature for another reason; instead of the short antennae of most crabs, this fellow has long ones fringed with rows of stiff hairs and grooved on one side. When pressed together, the antennae form a quadrangular air hose through which the crab breathes when buried in the mud.

On the coast of California the most common shore crabs are the purple shore crabs and the yellow shore crabs. They gather by thousands; frequently several hundred will be found together under one stone. Their backs are barely an inch in breadth and bear the lifelike face of a fat-cheeked, pudgy-faced person trying hard to look severe. Very different is the funny face on the carapace of a spiny-legged member of the spider crab group in Mexico; the back of this crab resembles the face of an Indian with narrowed eyes, high cheekbones, and a wide mouth. Even more striking and amusing is the face on the back of a spider crab from our Atlantic coast, particularly abundant in Chesapeake Bay. Instead of a dour, lugubrious face such as that on the back of the masked crab, this spider crab's mask is the face of a broad-cheeked yokel with long upper

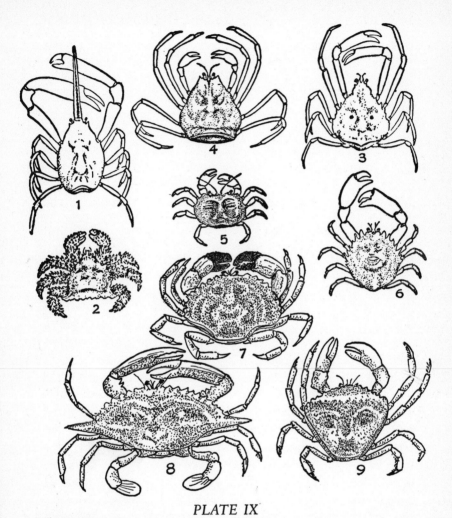

PLATE IX

1. Masked crab, Europe   2. The Indian from Mexico   3. Simple
Simon spider crab   4. Devil crab of China   5. Sleepyhead from
Florida   6. Happy Jack   7. Mr. Morro of Cuba   8. The face on
the blue crab   9. California mud crab

lip, smiling mouth, staring eyes, and a forehead topped by a peaked cap.

We are all familiar with the demoniac-looking faces so popular with Chinese artists and represented on Japanese masks. These look like genuine devils with crossed eyes, snarling mouth, puffy cheeks and sharp teeth. The Orientals got the idea for these fearsome faces from crabs. We have only to look at one of the huge masked spider crabs of Oriental waters to realize that the faces they bear on their shells are almost identical with the demons pictured in Chinese and Japanese art. There is the same wide mouth with lips drawn back to reveal fanglike teeth, the same great upper lip, bulging jowls, and the same cruel, slanting eyes. In sharp contrast to this "devil crab" of China and Japan is a jolly little spider crab from Florida whose back bears the face of a good-natured elf.

Why Mother Nature should have seen fit to decorate crabs' backs with funny faces is a mystery. Certainly these shell portraits are neither an advantage nor a disadvantage to the crabs. But it is no more of a puzzle than rock formations often being perfect profiles of human faces. Apparently it is just one of those things that no one can explain; but it can scarcely be passed off as a mere chance or coincidence.

22

Crabs: Granddaddy Horsefoot

ALONG our Atlantic coast from Maine to Florida the most conspicuous objects cast up by the waves are the cast-off shells of the remarkable creatures commonly known as horsefoot crabs, horseshoe crabs, or king crabs. All three names are misnomers, for the strange creature is not a crab; neither is it a lobster, a shrimp, or even a near relative of these animals. It is not even a crustacean, but it is closely related to the scorpions and spiders; the horsefoot's nearest relative is the ugly and repulsive-looking whip scorpion or, as it is called in Florida, the "grampus," a menacing and poisonous creature. In reality the grampus is harmless, its savage appearance being all a bluff. The so-called "stinger" on the end of the abdomen is merely a soft, fleshy appendage and the crablike front claws are incapable of pinching one hard enough to draw blood.

At first sight there may not seem to be much similarity between the horsefoot crab and the whip scorpion, but if we compare the underside of old Granddaddy Horsefoot with the underside of a scorpion we will find them very much alike. Both have pincer-claws on the first pair of legs, although the horsefoot crab has small pincers on all

but the last legs, which end in narrow oval plates. Both
creatures have eyes set in the head, not on stalks like those
of crustaceans, and, like the scorpions and spiders, the
horsefoot has an additional pair of small eyes near the
front of its head.

Although some crustaceans have long tails, none can
boast of such a caudal appendage as that of the horsefoot
crab: a hard, triangular spike with finely serrated edges
which is the creature's only means of defense. To be sure,

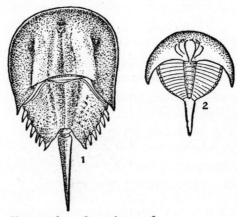

1. *King crab, or horsefoot crab*
2. *Ancestor of the horsefoot crab (eurypterid)*

it is not much of a weapon, but when swung viciously back
and forth, much in the manner of a broadsword, it is
capable of lacerating a man's skin and causing painful,
though superficial wounds. The tail also serves a very different and even more important purpose. When turned
upon its back the crab would be as helpless as an upside-
down sea turtle, were it not for its tail. Swinging it to
one side and forcing its tip into the sand, the creature will
use the tail as a lever, turning itself right side up in a
few seconds.

Seen from above, all similarity between the horsefoot crab and the scorpion disappears, but this is mainly because the creature's true body is concealed by the hard, semicircular carapace, which is hinged at the division of the thorax and abdomen. But if we examine the posterior part of the shell we will find depressions that are vestiges of six abdominal joints like those on the abdomen of the scorpion. However, external resemblances are usually so superficial that scientists give them little attention, classifying the animals by their internal anatomy. The internal structure of this crab is quite different from that of any living creatures other than the class which comprises spiders, mites and scorpions. Because it differs in many details from the other members of this class, it has been given a sub-class, as well as a separate genus, known as *Limulus,* which contains only two species, one being American, the other Asiatic.

Although the empty shells of the *Limulus* are common, living specimens are seldom found upon the beaches, and many people never have seen a live one, for the strange creatures live buried in sand beneath the low-water mark. If you wade about in shallow water or walk across a sand bar exposed by the ebbing tide, you may see odd markings or trails looking as though someone had dragged a shovel or a hoe across the sand. If you follow one of these tracks until it comes to an end and then dig into the sand, the chances are that you will uncover a live horsefoot crab. Unlike the pale-colored castoff skins that weigh very little, the living specimens are dark reddish-brown or greenish-brown and are quite heavy, for they contain a lot of flesh besides the internal organs, and are filled with water.

As you examine the strange creature, holding it by the tail while it moves its ten legs helplessly and the plates on the abdomen flap back and forth, you will wonder how on earth the clumsy creatures manage to shed their hard skins and leave them intact, with every detail perfect. If you carefully inspect the castoff skins you will note a narrow slit along the front edge of the carapace; incredible as it may seem, it is through this small and scarcely noticeable opening that the creature crawls and wriggles out of its overgrown shell.

This is not a difficult feat, for, as in the case of shedding lobsters and crabs, the new skin is soft and flexible within the old shell; several days are required for the new covering to become a hard, protective shell. In addition to serving as protection, the broad convex carapace with its thickened front edge is the creature's shovel. Pushing this into the sand by means of its feet and the broad gill cover plates on its abdomen, and forcing the damp sand backwards with its paddle-tipped pair of legs, even a large horsefoot crab will disappear quickly, completely buried from sight. Never intentionally will it reappear during the daytime; it will spend its days beneath the surface of the sand, constantly pushing forward, grubbing for worms and the other small fry upon which it feeds. If by chance the odd creature is forced to emerge, it will go sliding off, half-swimming, half-crawling close to the bottom, until it digs in again.

After nightfall they emerge from their burrows and actually frolic about in the water. Rearing themselves up on their strong tails they give a sudden jerk, kick themselves upward, and go paddling off quite swiftly; gradually they sink until they reach the bottom; then the performance is repeated. Although their progress through the water can scarcely be called swimming, they manage to travel rapidly, propelling themselves by their abdominal plates and paddle-like hind legs, moving in a series of short, jerky spurts.

Another curious aspect of these strange sea creatures is their custom of laying eggs on land. During the breeding season, hundreds of these crabs crawl from the water like so many sea turtles, and, like turtles, deposit their eggs in hollows scraped in the sand where they leave the eggs to their fate. Sea turtles' eggs remain in their sand nest until the baby turtles hatch out and hurry to the protection of the sea. But the eggs of the horsefoot crabs, blown by the wind, may often be found rolling about the beach like marbles. They become transparent as the embryo develops; each contains a baby horsefoot plainly visible within. When at last the spheres break open, the youngsters hatching out look like their parents, except that they have no tails; those do not appear until after the young have shed their baby skins and acquired a tougher shell.

The flesh of these creatures is better-tasting than that of lobsters or real crabs, but there is very little of it, and man uses the horsefoot crab only as fertilizer. Millions of the creatures have been captured and destroyed for this purpose; in many places where they once were plentiful they are now almost extinct.

Interesting as they are in appearance and habits, the most extraordinary fact about the horsefoot crabs is that they are, in a way, living fossils. They are the descendants of similar sea creatures known as eurypterids, which swarmed in the oceans during the Cambrian period.

Aside from the Foraminifera, which were described in the first chapter, the horsefoot crabs' ancestors were the most ancient denizens of the sea. Genealogically they are one of the "first families" of sea creatures. Hence it is quite fitting that they should actually have blue blood. What a great pity it is that these granddaddies of the sea should meet such an ignominious fate—that of being used for fertilizer!

23

Partnerships in the Sea

AMONG the features of marine life that command attention are the partnerships formed between creatures from totally different groups of animals, and even between animals and marine plants. Some of these partnerships are indeed puzzling; many are of obvious benefit to one or both partners, but others appear to be of no advantage to either, and several seem to hinder the associated creatures. A number of these underseas alliances are —like human ones—entered into for some specific but temporary purpose; many others endure for the lifetime of one or both of the partners.

It is not difficult to find and study one of these odd unions. If you examine the underside of a starfish in a tide pool, you doubtless will discover some minute serpent starfish making themselves at home in the sucker-lined grooves of the starfish's arms, where they remain, like invited guests, enjoying their host's hospitality. The chances are that small, shrimplike crustaceans and crabs will also be living unmolested among the suckers and spines of the starfish. Perhaps these partners of the sea stars find it to their advantage to be chummy with their hosts, upon whose crumbs they find easy dining. Since they act as scavengers and house cleaners, the sea stars benefit by their presence.

Even the spiny sea urchins have their partners in the form of tiny crustaceans. Although, as mentioned in Chapter 10, the sea urchins and sand dollars are equipped with many small nippers and other appendages to keep their surfaces clean, the hosts never disturb the visiting crabs and shrimps. The sea urchins realize that these chaps also aid in the house-cleaning job, and they pay them with minute scraps from their meals.

No one would expect the big black sea urchins, with their long, poisonous, needle-like spines, to have partners, since practically all other sea creatures give them a wide berth. However, the young sea crayfish or spiny lobsters consider them very useful chums, finding a safe refuge among the urchins' bristling spines, which cannot penetrate their shells. The sea urchins also benefit from the merger, for the spiny lobsters are sloppy in their table manners and their wasted food helps to fill the stomachs of the urchins.

Another group of the echinoderm family, the holothurians, or "sea cucumbers," have their partners too. Certain species are never found without serpent starfish and gaudy brittle stars clinging to them, and others apparently cannot exist unless associated with certain sea plants.

Among the flowerlike sea anemones we find the most astonishing undersea partnerships; these lovely creatures seem to have a mania for coöperating and merging with other creatures. No one can explain why or how these strange partnerships first started, but sea creatures apparently discovered ages ago that they were mutually advantageous and that certain combinations of habits and

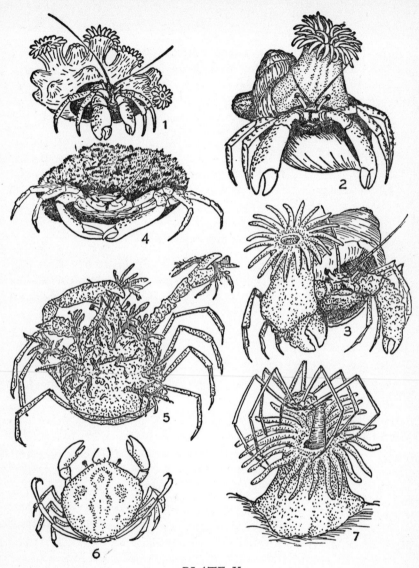

PLATE X

1. *Hermit crab in anemone house* 2. *Hermit crab with anemone planted on shell* 3. *Hermit crab with anemone on large claw* 4. *The crab that lives in a sponge* 5. *The spider-crab gardener* 6. *Oyster crab (female)* 7. *Pycnogonid pumping out an anemone*

inclinations could result in two living as cheaply and far more easily than one.

Various species of sea anemones habitually attach themselves to the shells of living mollusks and hitchhike here and there. This arrangement is of great advantage to the anemone who thus obtains a more adequate food supply than it would if attached to an immovable object in a fixed locality; probably the sea shell finds its anemone rider with its poisonous lasso-threads a helpful ally for keeping the shell's enemies at a respectful distance.

One of the most remarkable mergers is between the sea anemones and certain fishes and shrimps that actually live in the stomachs of the anemones. One shrimplike animal which habitually makes its home in the anemone's stomach cavity is the same color as its host, and for some curious reason is never digested. Of course this unusual habitation affords the crustacean an adequate and steady food supply, but it is difficult to understand how or why the anemone benefits, unless the inhabitant of its stomach relieves indigestion by consuming the surplus food the anemone has swallowed.

Even stranger is the partnership of certain anemones and fish, which, like the shrimp, live in the anemones' stomachs. One giant sea anemone, a species prevalent on the Great Barrier Reef of Australia, permits the brightly colored coral fish to swim in and out of its mouth at will, and never harms them, despite the fact that its everyday food consists of other fish rendered helpless by its stinging organs. In this case the coral fish are not actual residents of the anemone's interior, but use it as a refuge from their enemies, who will not venture within reach of their host's deadly stings. A family of fish—known as *Fierasferidae*—are seldom found except as partners of sea anemones and sea cucumbers, and spend their lives in the stomachs of their hosts. On rare occasions they venture out, but at the first sign of danger they dash back into the mouths of their anemone or holothurian friends.

Why the anemone should allow its stomach to serve as a fortress for the protection of fish instead of devouring them is as baffling a puzzle as why certain sea anemones select the glass rope sponges of Japan for partners. These large anemones have never been found elsewhere than attached to the sponge; conversely, it is very seldom that a glass sponge is found without its attendant anemones. In fact, for many years the glasslike roots of the sponge were mistaken for the roots of the anemones. The lovely Venus's-flower-basket sponge also has its partners, although in this case they are a species of shrimp. So prevalent is this partnership that one seldom sees a preserved specimen of flower-basket sponge that does not contain the desiccated bodies of its shrimp partners.

Even stranger is the amicable understanding between sea anemones and the odd creatures known as pycnogonids, or sea spiders. The sea spiders are not true spiders, but belong to an order of their own. Not only do they lack all breathing organs, but they have no real body; their circulatory and nervous systems, as well as their stomachs, are in their legs; their eggs are laid through the leg joints. Yet they have four eyes which, to complete the incongruity of the creatures' makeup, are situated at the tip of the pycnogonid's long snout.

Perhaps Nature designed these weird creatures for the sole purpose of providing partners for sea anemones, or at least to act as living stomach pumps for the flowerlike creatures. The long-legged freaks depend for a living upon the contents of the anemones' stomachs. It is fascinating to watch the repulsive-looking creatures in action, and as they are usually found wherever there are sea anemones, you may have a chance to witness the proceedings in some shady tide pool.

Moving slowly and deliberately, raised high on its long legs, the pycnogonid appears from some hidden lair and advances toward a sea anemone that has just finished eating a good meal. The strange creature steps upon the tentacles of the anemone, which remains fully expanded with its stinging threads withdrawn. At the first touch of any other creature, the petal-like tentacles would be withdrawn, and dozens of stinging organs would dart in every direction to drive off any possible foe. As the sea spider reaches the center of the anemone, it comes to a stop, bends its long snout downward, plunges it into the anemone's mouth, and proceeds to suck up the contents of the stomach. Often a pycnogonid will use its living stomach pump on several anemones before its appetite is satisfied. Then it goes stalking off on tiptoe to its den.

No one has yet been able to offer a logical reason for the anemone's submission to being literally pumped dry by the weird pycnogonids. Possibly some fluid is excreted that acts as an anesthetic and stupefies the anemone. Or perhaps anemones are gluttonous and, having eaten to excess, are glad to be relieved of the contents of their overloaded stomachs. One guess is as good as another.

Hermit crabs are the most common partners of the sea anemones; it is not unusual to see a hermit crab scuttling about in a sea shell with one or several anemones attached to its surface. In all probability this alliance came about through a crab's taking possession of a shell already decorated with anemones. As the crab was protected from the anemone's stings by hard armor, the occupant of the shell had no reason to pluck the squatter from his roof. He must have quickly discovered that the anemone decorating his shell house was useful protection from his natural en-

emies, for when the crabs outgrow their shells and are
compelled to find new quarters, they carefully remove the
anemones from the abandoned shell and transplant them
to the new one. Being trundled about has its advantages
for the anemone; whenever the hermit crab has had a meal
there are fragments of food floating within reach of the
anemone's tentacles. By adhering to a shell inhabited by
a hermit crab, the anemone is given a free ride, as well as
free lunches.

Just how this partnership began is mere speculation,
but for as long as man has taken notice of sea creatures,
there have been certain species of sea anemones and certain species of hermit crabs that are invariable partners.
So long have the two widely different creatures been associated that some anemones are found only on the shells of
certain hermit crabs. On the other hand, many hermit
crabs are not at all demanding, and seem perfectly satisfied with any kind of anemone on their shells.

The intimate relationship between sea anemones and
hermit crabs is amazing. One species of anemone is always attached to the lip of the shell, where its tentacles
reach the crab's mouth, and the two partners share their
meals, dining at the same table. Some hermit crabs transplant an anemone to their large claw, where it is most useful, for when the crab backs into its shell and closes the
aperture with its large claw, the anemone is well placed
as a guardian, and there it defies any creature to brave its
stings. A crab found in the Pacific has a somewhat similar
habit, but this chap, who is related to our spider crabs,
goes much further than the hermit with the anemone
watchdog; it plants an anemone on each of its large claws,
thus making them more dangerous weapons than Mother
Nature designed.

Since crabs must change their skins from time to time,

they are forced to transplant their anemone partners to their new ones, a task performed without injuring the anemone. To remove an anemone from a shell is a difficult task; apparently the anemone realizes that the crab is doing it a good turn, for it voluntarily loosens its grip at the crab's touch.

Certain species of hermit crabs never need to transplant their anemone friend; the parasite dissolves the crab's shell and in its place forms a horny space that fits the body of the crab. As the crab grows, the anemone enlarges the cavity in its base to accommodate the increased size of its tenant. This unusual partnership savors of real intelligence and mutual understanding, yet it is not an uncommon arrangement. In fairly deep water off our Atlantic coast a brilliant red species of sea anemone exists solely as a living home for a species of hermit crab. And the "velvet cloak" anemone of European seas invariably houses a good-sized hermit crab.

Tastes differ among these sea creatures as much as among the higher animals, and even though most crabs find anemones their best friends, a few prefer sponges. Because the sponges possess stinging organs, they are avoided by most other creatures. Hence, the crabs harboring sponges on their backs are doubly protected. Moreover, the sponges serve as a camouflage, and—unless in motion—a crab with sponges on its back is indistinguishable from an ordinary sponge. Just as the crabs with sea anemone partners are forced to transplant them when the crabs, change their skins, so those carrying sponges must transplant each time they molt.

Some species of crabs have done away with this somewhat difficult task by carrying a piece of sponge wherever they go, holding it in position over their bodies with the last pairs of legs especially provided for that purpose by

Nature. Frequently the sponge grows more rapidly than the crab and completely hides its host, who dwells within a recess in the bottom of the sponge. Just as some species of hermit crabs are never found without certain sea anemone partners, so certain species of true crabs are never found except in association with particular sponges. Like the anemones that absorb the shells and form homes for hermit crabs, certain gaudy red or orange sponges destroy the acquired sea shell of hermit crabs and provide a substitute recess in their bases so that the hermit never has to change its quarters as its size increases.

The oyster crabs—or "peacrabs"—form interesting partnerships with oysters. The most remarkable feature of this partnership is that only the females live in the oysters; the males live a normal life in the sea and look very much like other small crabs, except for their elongated hind legs. If you examine oyster crabs, you will find that they are quite different from ordinary crabs. Their shells are soft, like those of shedder crabs; within an oyster, they have no need for protective armor. Since they have very little need for their legs, these have become small, weak, and practically useless for movement.

In addition to the oyster crab, the females of several other species live in mussels, scallops, and different bivalve shells. Another species—with an elongated body and downy surface—prefers the underground tubes of marine worms. In this case, both the male and the female crabs become partners of the worms and are seldom if ever found outside of the parchmentlike tubes. It is impossible for them to desert their worm partner—even if they wished to—for as they grow up they become much too large to escape through the small chimneylike openings of the worm's tube.

Even stranger is the association of a certain oceanic

shrimp with the purple shell of the *Janthina.* This shell
floats at the surface of the sea, where it is supported by a
buoyant raft formed with bubbles of mucus in which the
shell lays its eggs.* The majority of these rafts carry one
or two passengers—shrimplike crustaceans, colored purple
and blue exactly like the raft and the shell; thus they are
scarcely discernible.

The sea creatures least likely to have partners are the
jellyfish with their deadly stinging organs. But there are
certain fish which are their habitual chums. One large,
oceanic jellyfish, whose stinging tentacles will kill ordinary fish, is the partner of the young tuna; it is seldom
that one of these huge jellyfish can be found without a
number of the young tuna beneath it, sheltered safely from
their enemies. Another species of jellyfish even permits
certain fish to seek refuge within the body cavity, and
specimens have been found containing more than one
hundred active small fish. Even that most deadly of all
the jellyfish group—the Portuguese man-of-war—has its
partners; several species of fish covered with an impervi-
ous coating of slime are immune to the man-of-war's stings.
The commonest of these is the pastor fish, who finds the
powerful stinging organs of the man-of-war act as a perfect
barrier to its foes while it dines freely on the bits of food
dropped by its protector.

All partnerships I have mentioned are associations
between marine animals, but a number of sea creatures
select plants for life partners. Conspicuous among these
are the spider crabs. Lacking powerful nipper claws and
being rather slow-moving creatures, the majority seek
safety by burying themselves in mud or hiding in holes
and crevices of rocks and coral; others spend most of their
lives within certain kinds of sponges. But some crabs rely

* See: *Strange Sea Shells and Their Stories.*

entirely upon camouflage for safety and achieve the desired result by planting seaweed or algae upon the shells. No human gardener is more expert at cultivating terrestrial plants than these crustaceans. Frequently the back of one of these spider crabs will be completely hidden beneath a mass of algae, hydroids, bryozoans, and other marine growths.

It is a most interesting and amazing sight to watch one of these ten-legged gardeners at work. Hunting about until he finds just the right plant or growth he wants, he carefully cuts it off near the base. Holding the cutting in one claw, he places the nipped-off end in his mouth. He does not eat it; he merely prepares the cutting for planting and chews at it until it is frayed and soft, in the meantime coating it with a gluelike substance secreted from glands in his mouth. This having been accomplished, he lifts the prepared cutting, places it in the desired position on his back, and presses the sticky base firmly against the short, stiff bristles of his shell. By some mysterious sense he seems to know exactly where to set out each cutting, for he cannot possibly see what he is doing. Frequently he will use both his claws, holding and setting out a prepared cutting in each one.

It seems unbelievable that a creature such as a mere crab should possess the intelligence to transplant sea growths to his shell to disguise himself as a marine plant. But it is even more astonishing to find that he is careful to transplant only growths that will harmonize with his environment. If his haunts are in an area where the majority of the weeds are dark brown, he will hunt about until he finds dark-brown plants for his garden. If the general tone of the weed growths is greenish, he will select green plants. And if the sea bottom is overgrown with weeds and hydroids of various hues, he will pick and choose, transplanting some of each color in exactly the proper proportions and combinations to blend with his surroundings.

If a spider crab, carrying on his back a garden of plants of a certain color and type, is placed in an aquarium where there are growths of other hues and forms, he will immediately tear off the plants on his back and replace them with cuttings from the growths surrounding him. He never makes a mistake; if he happens to have been living in an area where corallines abound and he finds himself confined amid soft weeds and leafy algae, he will at once uproot the corallines on his shell and replace them with the algae.

Almost as astounding as these crab agriculturists are the spider crabs that cover their backs, claws, and legs with small pebbles, fragments of broken shells, coral, and similar debris; they wedge these into place among the bristles of their shells, thus transforming themselves into living sections of the sea floor where they live.

Another of the mutual benefit associations is the one existing between certain algae and a species of European marine worm—known to scientists as *Convoluta*. So intimate and long-standing is their association that one cannot exist without the other. In their infancy the *Convoluta* feeds upon other animals and plants, exactly as do worms; but it also swallows quantities of the minute, green, single-celled plants present in the water. These, however, are never digested but thrive and multiply within the internal organs of the worms until the latter become entirely green and are perfectly camouflaged. By this time the worms are subsisting entirely upon the scratchy material produced by the algae, and their internal organs have been adapted to this process. In order to produce the food for the worms, the algae must be exposed to sunlight; each time the tide ebbs, hundreds of the green worms emerge from their burrows and rest on the bottom to permit their internal algae to absorb the sunshine through the shallow water. Then, as the tide turns, they return to the burrows, only to repeat the process at the next ebb tide. So fixed is this habit —essential to the existence of both partners—that when confined in an aquarium, where there is no tide, the worms will rise and fall twice a day, exactly as if the tide were rising and ebbing within the walls of glass.

24

Missing Links

SOME of our sea dwellers are orphans; they have no near relatives among the marine invertebrates. But these creatures all have certain characteristics indicating that they are maritime missing links—forms of life connecting the invertebrates with the vertebrates.

All higher forms of animal life, from fish to man, have a backbone or spinal column with nerves branching to the various parts of the body; a brain that controls the nerves; well-developed, single-lens eyes; a circulatory system through which blood or a similar fluid is pumped by a heart or a similar organ; a respiratory system, and a complex digestive system. The invertebrates lack the spinal cord; a nerve center, or ganglion, takes the place of a brain; the eyes as a rule are rudimentary and often compound; there is no true heart or circulatory system; and the digestive system may consist of a single tube, or it may be quite complex, with stomach, liver, and intestines.

These sea orphans have a large master nerve or notochord serving as a spinal cord; nerves branch from this and are controlled by a rudimentary brain. There is a well-developed circulatory system, a respiratory system with gill-slots, well-developed, single-lens eyes, and a digestive tract. The sea squirts, or ascidians, described in Chapter 6, belong in this group of missing links of the sea; but in their case it is the larval forms that have characteristics—lacking in the adults—indicating a transition stage toward the vertebrates. In other words the ascidians—in contrast to most of these missing links—are retrogressing, instead of advancing on the road to a higher status in the animal kingdom.

These misfits belong in the large group called Chordata (which also includes the vertebrates), and are classed as members of the protochordates, animals whose structures have some features characteristic of the true vertebrates. They possess the rudimentary spinal cord known as the notochord, a dorsal nerve-cord with a nerve canal, a series of paired gill openings, a nerve-control organ or brain, an excellent circulatory system, and well-developed digestive tracts, with the blood produced by the alimentary tract passing through the liver prior to circulation.

Among the most interesting members of this group are the odd burrowing creatures known as *Phoronis*. These are elongated, wormlike animals which also resemble some of the free-swimming sea anemones. They are five or six inches in length, with a straight body swollen or bulbous at the lower end, and pink in color at the upper end, shading to red or yellow. At the upper extremity there is a fringe of long, soft tentacles encircling a horseshoe-shaped ridge about the mouth, each tentacle covered with cilia. The adult *Phoronis* lives buried up to the neck in sand or mud, where it is securely anchored by the bulbous lower end of the body. The larval form, however, is a free-swimming creature, quite different in appearance from its parents. It has a short body that is swollen or bulbous at the upper end, where the mouth, with its circle

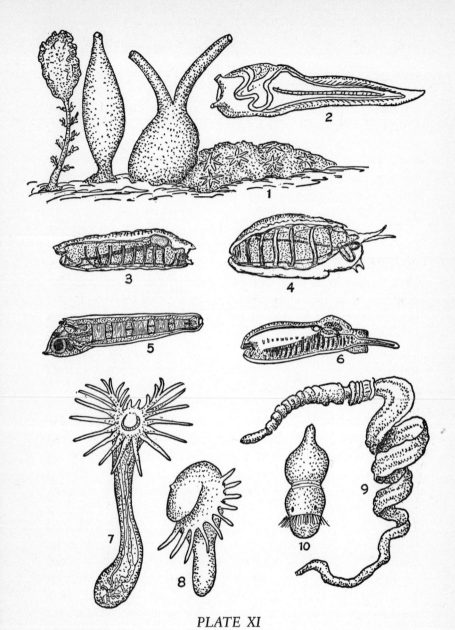

PLATE XI

1. *Ascidians, or sea squirts*   2. *Larva of an ascidian*   3, 4, 5, 6. *Salpas*
7. *Phoronis*   8. *Larva of Phoronis*   9. *Acorn worm*   10. *Larva of*
acorn worm

of short tentacles, is completely concealed beneath a hood-like growth.

At a certain stage of its growth, a tubelike opening appears on one side of the body just below the tentacles. The larva then abandons its free-swimming life and, settling to the bottom of the sea, anchors itself in the sand. Then an amazing event takes place. The tubular opening in the body-wall suddenly turns inside out and the intestine breaks away from the old mouth and enters the tube, thus forming a new mouth. At the same time the hood-like covering, the eyes, and the nerve center are swallowed up by the new mouth and digested. Then the weird creature devours its own tentacles, which are soon replaced by the circle of tentacles about the new adult's mouth— which has also developed a double rudimentary notochord! These truly remarkable animals are common near the low-water mark on the sand flats of our southern states, where thousands are dug up as "fish worms," the diggers never realizing that the "worms" are among the most amazing of all sea creatures.

Inhabiting the same areas as the *Phoronis,* and also extensively used as fish bait, are the creatures known as acorn worms, which are fully as strange as the *Phoronis*— and in some respects even more astonishing. In appearance they are more wormlike; they are long and slender, with a coiled body and a huge, tapering, cylindrical snout. Below this pink snout is an orange-yellow collar that in some specimens is bright red; the rest of the body is yellow, mottled with orange or red. Although the creature is usually little more than six inches in length, it has the power to elongate itself enormously when disturbed. The big snout is the acorn worm's pick and shovel; with it the creature can burrow with astonishing speed. Filling it with water for stiffening, the animal forces it into the sand; then he expands it at the tip, thus anchoring it; he then draws the body forward, forces the nose still deeper, and repeats the operation until completely buried.

If we examine an acorn worm carefully we will find that it is divided into three distinct sections; the body, the neck or collar, and the big snout. In some species this is acorn-shaped; hence the common name. The mouth is on one side of the narrow neck, between the collar and proboscis, and here, in connection with the pharynx, are vestiges of a notochord. Throughout the length of the body and on either side there are gill slots; behind these are liver sacs. On the back of the collar is a nerve canal extending backward like a spinal cord, with smaller nerves leading to various parts of the animal. In addition, there is a kidney and a ventral and a dorsal artery or blood vessel extending the entire length of the body. As in the case of many of these misfit creatures, the free-swimming young acorn worms are totally different from the adults, being short and stubby and more or less top-shaped. They have a slightly constricted "belt" about the middle, and with a fringe of vibratory swimming hairs near one end.

Still another of these interesting maritime missing links is the creature called *Salpa*. In these animals the body is usually more or less elliptical and cylindrical in section; they are transparent, so that the internal organs are plainly visible. The *Salpas* are highly luminous at night and abound in the open sea. They are small creatures, seldom over eight inches in length, and are free-swimming; they are jet-propelled, and travel by drawing in water at one end and forcing it out the other.

Another peculiar feature of the *Salpas* is that the generations alternate, one producing solitary animals, the next, aggregated individuals. Although apparently simple little creatures, the *Salpas* have many of the characteristics of the other links between the invertebrates and the verte-brates. But even more remarkable is the manner in which the minute, newly produced young migrate to the backs of their parents and there attach themselves in three abso-lutely regular rows. As one zoologist states, "It is one of the most astonishing mysteries that zoology affords."

25

Creatures of the Great Depths

THERE are even stranger and more numerous forms of marine life dwelling in the abysmal depths of the oceans than in the shallower parts of the sea. Despite the dredging and trawling done by the United States Fish Commission and scientific organizations and despite observations by men who have descended to great depths, little is known regarding the creatures inhabiting the deeper portions of the sea. This is scarcely surprising when we stop to consider the limitations of deep-sea explorations. Dredging has long been carried on over thousands of square miles of the bottom of the sea, yet the total area that has been covered is infinitesimal. Moreover, there is not one chance in a thousand that a dredge or trawl will bring up any substantial portion of the creatures living on the ocean's floor. Although men who have been lowered hundreds of fathoms below the surface of the sea in bathyspheres have observed and described some new sea creatures, they have descended only a short distance where the sea is thousands of fathoms deep.

However, limited as the deep-sea explorations have been, we have learned a great deal about animal life at depths. We know that there are the same forms of marine animals as those found in shallower water: crustaceans, gorgonians, sea anemones, sponges, holothurians, worms, shells, fish, and representatives of other groups. Some are grotesque creatures. Some are almost exact counterparts of the shallow-water members of their groups. And practically all are luminous, and often display brilliant rows or masses of lights shining from their bodies. Whether these lights illuminate the Stygian blackness of the great depths, protect the creatures from their enemies, or attract and dazzle their prey, no one knows.

A gorgonian: the sea feather

A curious thing about the deep-sea animals is that the fish are monstrosities as a rule, totally unlike fish of the shallower waters. But the majority of other forms of life differ only slightly from those of shoal water; only a scientist could distinguish a deep-sea starfish, sea urchin, crab or holothurian from similar creatures found just below the tidewater mark. Moreover, there are few known deep-sea animals not having counterparts among the sea creatures along our shores.

In the ocean depths where no light penetrates, eyesight is of little importance. Hence, many deep-sea animals are blind. On the other hand, many are gaudily colored, although in the perpetual blackness all colors should theoretically look the same. Why Nature should have lavished brilliant hues on these inhabitants of the deep is a mystery. My father once replied when someone asked him the reason, "It is just as easy for God to make a bright-colored creature as a dull-colored one."

There is misunderstanding regarding the terrific pressures at the great depths and the ability of animals to withstand such pressures, which often amount to five or six tons per square inch. One can calculate the water's pressure at any depth, for it increases fifteen pounds to the square inch every thirty-three feet. Thus at a depth of one hundred feet the water pressure would be about forty-five pounds to the square inch—about the limit a man in an ordinary diving suit can withstand. It is often asked why the deep-sea creatures are not crushed to pulp. The answer is that the pressure is the same inside and outside their bodies. Contrary to what people believe, an animal will not burst or explode when drawn to the surface from great depths; most of them collapse and become formless, pulpy masses of flesh when brought up. However, they do not always die when they rise toward the surface. Even fish whose air bladders may burst—thus releasing the contained gas —and who are unable to dive or sink to their deep-sea homes, may survive.

Many deep-sea creatures are able to adjust themselves to almost any depth. Thousands of the more common sea creatures found along our shores appear to do just as well at depths of 1000 fathoms or more as they do at tidewater level. Other creatures inhabiting the depths find no inconvenience in rising to the surface and returning to their deep-sea homes; innumerable species of deep-sea animals spend the day hundreds of thousands of fathoms down, yet regularly rise to the surface to spend the night.

Even more remarkable in their ability to adapt themselves to almost any pressure are the sea creatures that live at the bottom of the oceans in the adult stage, but whose larvae rise and swim about at the surface until maturity, when they descend and anchor themselves to the bottom of the sea. Many of the hydroids that produce jellyfish live at great depths—yet the offspring swim about at the sea's surface.

Some marine animals are just the reverse; that is, the fully grown creatures may live in shallow water, but the young prefer the great depths; there are a number of the delicate jellyfish that are perfectly at home several hundred fathoms beneath the surface. How they endure conditions under which other creatures immediately die is a mystery—one more of many that will never be solved until the sea herself reveals the answer from her store of ancient wisdom.

Index

Index

25

ABOUT THE AUTHOR

A. HYATT VERRILL was born in New Haven, Connecticut, in 1871. He was the son of the late Addison E. Verrill, the noted zoologist and geologist, who was professor of these subjects at Yale University for over forty years.

Mr. Verrill received his early scientific training in zoology and geology under his father and studied at the Yale School of Fine Arts. Although always maintaining his interest in these sciences and in art, he devoted his life to conducting explorations and expeditions into the jungles of tropical America, as well as to making archaeological investigations and excavations in the Andean regions of Peru, Bolivia, and Chile, and in Central America.

The list of his explorations over a period of almost fifty years was varied and fascinating. He tramped through the unknown jungles of Darien and the "forbidden" district of the Kunas in Panama. For nearly five years of his life he followed the jungle creeks and trails of British Guiana, visiting every tribe within the area and collecting specimens of their artifacts, weapons, and utensils. In Panama he discovered the remains of an unknown culture and carried on extensive excavations.

As a result of Mr. Verrill's expeditions, much valuable material in natural history, ethnology, geology, and archaeology has been added to various private and public museums in the United States and Europe.

He wrote a great many books dealing with his travels, discoveries, and experiences, as well as with natural history.

Among the latter is the STRANGE STORIES FROM NATURE SERIES, which includes the present volume.

As an artist, Mr. Verrill probably made a greater number of drawings for scientific works than any other illustrator. He did the natural history illustrations for Webster's International Dictionary and at one time made for the Museum of the American Indian a series of oil paintings from life, depicting the various South and Central American tribal types.

Mr. Verrill lived in England for a number of years and traveled extensively on the Continent. For many years he made his home in Lake Worth, Florida. He moved to Chiefland, Florida, several months before his death in November, 1954.

LIBERATORS AND HEROES OF SOUTH AMERICA

By MARION LANSING

Jacket in full color by Paul Quinn. Also illustrated from photographs $4.00

Some thirty years after the American Colonies had gained their independence from England, South America began her long and bloody struggle for freedom from the yoke of Spain. And just as the American Revolution gave us such great names as Paul Revere and Samuel Adams, so the Wars of Independence gave to South America the great national heroes whom she honors today.

Simón Bolívar, often called the "George Washington of South America" was, of course, the supreme genius of the Wars of Independence, but there were many others, of whom little is known, who played their part no less magnificently. Among them are: Miranda, Forerunner of Independence; San Martín, Savior of the South; Moreno, Champion of Free Speech; O'Higgins, Supreme Director of Chile; Santander, Man of Laws; and Paez, The Man on Horseback.

. . . "In this series of sixteen biographical sketches, Marion Lansing tells the story of the men who made possible these South American countries of today. It is a book of substance and style. It comprises a single story, and a great one it is, of sacrifice, devotion, adventure and the highest courage, one to be read and remembered wherever freedom is prized." . . . *New York Times.*

. . . "These sixteen biographies of South American heroes are the type of literature that will further Pan Americanism, for a knowledge of the history of a people and how it parallels our own aids in bringing understanding.

"Parallels there are, and described vividly. . . . Ragged troops that suffered terrors equal to Valley Forge, and battles as thrilling as Bunker Hill. And through it all the same desire for freedom from overseas tyrants." . . . *Philadelphia Record.*

My Jungle Trails

BY A. HYATT VERRILL

Illustrated from photographs and paintings by the author and
  Charles Livingston Bull $3.75

A. Hyatt Verrill's knowledge of Latin American jungles *is probably unexcelled by that of any scientist-explorer in the United States today,* writes Professor Kirtley F. Mather in recommending MY JUNGLE TRAILS for THE SCIENTIFIC BOOK CLUB, and he adds:

"Mr. Verrill's tales are far from humdrum and commonplace. He is an expert raconteur and he has selected from his rich store many vivid experiences that *hold the reader's interest as surely as the year's best detective story.* More than that, they are a means of insight into the ways of nature and man in tropical lowlands, which is far more realistic than that gained from the usual geographic or ethnological treatise.

"Even the city-bred must sense the lure of the jungles as he reads this splendid collection of narratives. . . . Adventures of all sorts are the inevitable by-products of the quests for rare animals or plants or for information concerning strange peoples beyond the frontiers of civilization. Perhaps it is because Mr. Verrill has sought something other than adventure that his narration rings so true."

MY JUNGLE TRAILS is based upon Mr. Verrill's experiences and adventures gained during nearly fifty years in which as naturalist, ethnologist, author and artist he has led expeditions into the unknown jungles of Darien, the "forbidden" districts of the Kunas in Panama, and followed the jungle creeks and trails of British Guiana and all the other countries of equatorial America.

"As Mr. Verrill looks back over almost half a century, this veteran wanderer finds adventurous tales to tell. He has brought together what are frankly the most unusual things that have happened to him to make a very interesting book. In strange hinterlands of Panama and Costa Rica, in Santo Domingo and the Lesser Antilles, and in the mysterious fastnesses of British Guiana, the author met with incidents which were sometimes exciting, sometimes amusing, sometimes puzzling and almost always unpredictable. The result is a variety which never lets the reader down."—*New York Herald-Tribune.*

Included in the AMERICAN LIBRARY ASSOCIATION BOOKLIST

FAMOUS LEADERS SERIES

Each one volume, cloth decorative, 12mo, illustrated by photographs.

By Charles H. L. Johnston:

FAMOUS CAVALRY LEADERS

FAMOUS INDIAN CHIEFS

FAMOUS SCOUTS

FAMOUS PRIVATEERSMEN AND ADVENTUR-
ERS OF THE SEA

FAMOUS FRONTIERSMEN AND HEROES OF
THE BORDER

FAMOUS DISCOVERERS AND EXPLORERS OF
AMERICA

FAMOUS GENERALS OF THE GREAT WAR

FAMOUS AMERICAN ATHLETES OF TODAY,
First Series.

FAMOUS AMERICAN ATHLETES OF TODAY,
Second Series.

FAMOUS AMERICAN ATHLETES OF TODAY,
Third Series. *By LeRoy Atkinson and Austen Lake*

FAMOUS AMERICAN ATHLETES OF TODAY,
Fourth Series. *By Charles H. L. Johnston*

FAMOUS AMERICAN ATHLETES OF TODAY,
Fifth Series. *By LeRoy Atkinson*

FAMOUS AMERICAN ATHLETES OF TODAY,
Sixth Series. *By Harold Kaese*

B-1

FAMOUS LEADERS SERIES (Cont.)

FAMOUS AMERICAN ATHLETES OF TODAY,
Seventh Series. *By Jerry Nason*

FAMOUS AMERICAN ATHLETES OF TODAY,
Eighth Series. *By Harold Kaese*

FAMOUS AMERICAN ATHLETES OF TODAY,
Ninth Series. *By Gordon Campbell*

FAMOUS AMERICAN ATHLETES OF TODAY,
Tenth Series. *By Al Hirshberg* and *Joe McKenney*

FAMOUS AMERICAN ATHLETES OF TODAY,
Eleventh Series. *By Frank Waldman*

FAMOUS AMERICAN ATHLETES OF TODAY,
Twelfth Series. *By Frank Waldman*

THE FOUNDERS OF AMERICA
THE BUILDERS OF AMERICA
FAMOUS LEADERS OF CHARACTER
By Edwin Wildman

FAMOUS LEADERS OF INDUSTRY
First Series. *By Edwin Wildman*
FAMOUS LEADERS OF INDUSTRY
Second Series. *By Edwin Wildman*
FAMOUS LEADERS OF INDUSTRY
Third Series. *By Trentwell M. White*
FAMOUS LEADERS OF INDUSTRY
Fourth Series. *By Harry Irving Shumway*
FAMOUS LEADERS OF INDUSTRY
Fifth Series. *By Joseph A. Moore*

FAMOUS AMERICAN MARINES
FAMOUS AMERICAN NAVAL OFFICERS
By Charles Lee Lewis

ISRAEL POTTER: His Fifty Years of Exile

 By Herman Melville

Illustrated by Frank T. Merrill, cloth, 12mo, $3.50

THE sea, as in all of Melville's novels, is the setting for this tale, and Israel's adventures on the *Bonhomme Richard* under John Paul Jones form a large portion of the action of the story. But in addition, Israel is at Bunker Hill, and at Paris when Benjamin Franklin was the darling of the French duchesses. Then there are the years of his exile in London—all in all, a lively tale.

During the seventy years that ISRAEL POTTER has been so unexplainably out of print, it has remained associated in the minds of Melville enthusiasts with the splendid pen portraits of Franklin, Paul Jones, and Ethan Allen. In this field of historical portraiture, Melville takes his place with Scott and Dumas. In the pages of ISRAEL POTTER, these three characters stand out as vividly as life. They were historical names, and Melville has made of them historical personages.

"It is a good thing to bring the book out again, so that it may be remembered with the finest works of an author of immortal stature."—*The Providence Journal.*

Seven of Melville's most popular titles are now available in a uniform binding. The titles are as follows:

Moby Dick	White Jacket
Typee	Mardi
Omoo	Redburn

Israel Potter